THE POETRY STORE

ABOUT PAUL COOKSON

Paul has worked as a poet in schools for over fifteen years. During that time he has visited thousands of schools, edited over thirty books and written loads of poems (some of them are even quite good).

He used to be a teacher. Now he has all the best bits about teaching like making children laugh, helping them to write their own poems, teaching achievement and enjoyment and most of all, having fun in school. Plus he can walk away at the end of the day, doesn't have to do any marking, fill in any forms or listen to Ofsted Inspectors.

Paul often performs with David Harmer, as 'Spill The Beans' in their rock and roll family poetry show and spends most of his time visiting schools and festivals all over the British Isles.

Sometimes he even goes home to Retford where his wife and two children ask who he is and whether he's brought any presents home.

If he has any spare time, Paul likes to go and watch Everton football club, play loud music, buy colourful shirts, read other people's books and play tennis and five-a-side football (but not all at the same time).

THE POETRY STORE

Your one-stop shop for poems!

Compiled by

Paul Cookson

Designer: Jane Hawkins

Published in Great Britain in 2005
by Hodder Children's Books

Reprinted in 2007

The right of Paul Cookson to be identified as the compiler
has been asserted by him in accordance with the
Copyright, Designs and Patents Act 1988

Cataloguing in Publication Data
The Poetry Store
1.Children's poetry, English
I. Cookson, Paul
821'.008

ISBN: 978 0340 893869

Printed and bound in Great Britain by Bookmarque Ltd, Croydon

Hodder Children's Books
338 Euston Road, London NW1 3BH

DEDICATED TO :

The real Mr. Moore (creaking down the corridor) and the staff and pupils of Carr Hill Primary School, Retford, Notts.

Contents

4 Playtimes at School

5 Teachers

6 Friends

10 Divali and Other Festivals

11 Animals and Birds

12 Pets

13 Space

14 Weather

20 Birthdays

21 Our Bodies

22 Sports

23 Hobbies

24 Toys

27 Feelings

INTRODUCTION

Hello and welcome to *The Poetry Store*!

Come in, browse awhile, look around, you're sure to find something you like.

If you're looking for a poem on a particular subject then the chances are that we have it covered in one of the thirty sections in this fantastic collection.

If you want a particular poet or genre (or if you are a teacher trying to find a haiku on a wet Wednesday morning for Literacy Hour) then try looking at the back at the specialised index and I'm sure you'll find what you are looking for.

If you just want some of the best poems around by some of the best poets around then you are in the right place.

Whatever your reasons for visiting *The Poetry Store* I know you'll find something you like, something that you will want to take away, something that you will want to share with others and something that will make you want to come back. Again and again and again.

It's that type of book, that type of store. Something for everyone – your one-stop shop of poetry delights.

See you soon,

Best wishes

Paul Cookson

20

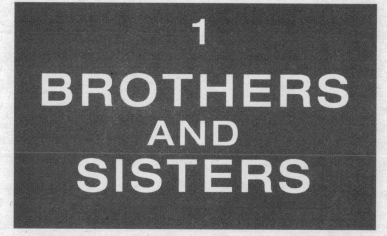

1
BROTHERS AND SISTERS

Grudges

It isn't fair...
that I must be in bed
for hours before,
that I get all the blame
and never her,
that she's allowed to choose
what she will wear,
it isn't fair!

It isn't right...
that she's allowed out
late at night,
that she can choose
when to switch off her light,
whenever there's a fight,
it isn't right!

It makes me mad...
that they think she's so good
and I'm so bad,
that she gets extra cash
for helping Dad,
that her old coats are all
I've ever had,
it makes me mad!

(I know I'm nine
and she is seventeen;
that's no excuse at all
for them to be so MEAN!)

Judith Nicholls

My Pain

It doesn't hurt with sudden screams,
like cuts, or stings, or scrapes.
It doesn't help to cover it
with bandages and tapes.

It doesn't make me howl like
I'm waiting for a shot,
or when I touch my finger to
the stove when I should not.

It isn't like those frozen brains
you get some summer day
when ice cream burns behind your eyes
then quickly melts away.

It's more a steady soreness,
like a nasty, nagging blister.
If you have got a pain like mine,
it's probably your sister.

Ted Scheu

Oh Yuk!
(An icky-sticky alphabet)

Aah... Boo! Coochie-coo
Did-Ems, Fluffy-bunny? Ga-ga-goo

Ho-ho, Iggle Jiggle
Klip-klop, Lollipop

Mummy wuvs oo!
Now, now... Oos a Pet?
Quiet, baby, don't fret.

Roly poly, Sweetie pie
Tickle tummy – My my!

Underneath his pillow
Very Wickle dreams, slip into his sleepy head
eX-tra special schemes.

Yes he is a treasure – *a treasure yes he is*
   Dozing in his blanket
Zizz Zizz Zizz.

Jan Dean

Prayer

Dear God,

Susie's mother is in hospital for tests.
She wants to have another baby
Because Susie's an only one
And she doesn't want her to be spoilt.

You're not supposed to get spoilt
If you have brothers and sisters.

Please help her, Lord,
Because you know Susie really wants a brother
And I do wish she could have one.

And if it's any help at all Lord –
Now that you've made absolutely sure
For six years, five months, twenty four days, three
    hours and two
minutes that I haven't been spoilt –

She can have mine.

Amen

Daphne Kitching

He and She

She took after their father,
Hair like a tangle of wire.
He took after their mother,
A dreamer who curled by the fire.

She chose games that were rowdy,
Borrowed his planes and his cars.
He gazed out of the window,
Riding the moon and the stars.

She would rage like a tiger,
Fight him with fists and with hate.
He would smoulder in silence,
Patiently, bitterly wait.

She ran wild in the playground,
Shouting her threats at the boys.
He crept under the oak tree
Guarding his thoughts from the noise.

She was chased through the schoolyard,
Taunted and trapped till she cried.
He was a powerful stranger,
A hero who flew to her side.

She took after their father,
He took after their mother,
Both of them bloodied and smiling,
Proud to be sister and brother.

Clare Bevan

My Little Sister

I may be small,
Wouldn't harm a flea,
But you'd better not lay a finger on me.
Got no weapons,
Don't play tough,
But I've got a sister, and that's enough.

Touch my bike,
Steal my books,
My little sister give you one of her looks.
If I just scream
Or I just shout,
My little sister gonna sort you out.

My little sister
My skin-and-blister,
My little sister gonna sort you out.

She ain't cute,
She ain't sweet,
Watch her fists and she'll use her feet.
She's no angel,
Plays no harp,
Files her nails till they're razor sharp.

First you're up,
Then laid flat,
You'd better go put a plaster on that.
Had enough?

Want some more?
... She'll be a terror by the time she's four.

My little sister,
My skin-and-blister,
She'll be a terror by the time she's four.

Paul Bright

A Boy to his Older Sister

Of course I won't tell Kevan
That I caught you kissing Sid
    Promises last for ever
And they only cost of five quid.

Gareth Owen

Kennings for Kevin

nail nibbler
  homework scribbler
veg refuser
  school tie loser

scab scratcher
  zapper snatcher
pimple picker
  bogey flicker

big wind breaker
  my things taker
shandy slurper
  belch and burper

rude word curser
  but much worser

big hair gel-er
  bad joke teller
mirror starer
  couldn't carer

sofa sprawler
  in love faller
bathroom hogger
  girlfriend snogger

yes that is him
  that's our Kevin
my big brother
  total nutter

David Horner

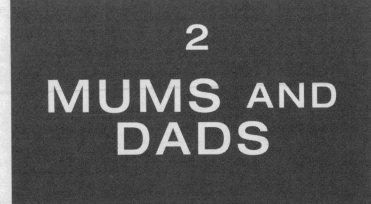

2
MUMS AND DADS

Sweet and Low

Sweet and low, sweet and low,
Wind of the western sea,
Low, low breathe and blow,
Wind of the western sea!
Over the rolling waters go,
Come from the dying moon and blow,
Blow him again to me;
While my little one, while my pretty one, sleeps.

Sleep and rest, sleep and rest,
Father will come to thee soon;
Rest, rest, on mother's breast,
Father will come to thee soon;
Father will come to his babe in the nest,
Silver sails all out of the west
Under the silver moon:
Sleep my little one, sleep, my pretty one, sleep.

Alfred, Lord Tennyson

Love Me Mum

Love me
Even though I sulk for days.
Love me
Even when I answer back.
Love me
Even when I get in trouble.
Love me Mum
For I love you.

I love you
Even when I rant and rave.
I love you
Even when I'm in a mood.
I love you
Even when I'm nagging on.
I love you
For I'm your mum.

Brenda Williams

My Mum

My mum makes cakes
My mum sews clothes
My mum mends stuff
My mum is good at
Masses of things

Under the stairs there's
Underwear for mending
Upholstery for curtaining
Undercoat for painting
Under the bed there's
Uniforms for washing
Undisturbed fluff for vacuuming
Umpteen things to do, but still

My mum kicks footballs
My mum feeds ducks
My mum runs races, so
My mum's the best!

Suzanne Elvidge

Parent Problem Solved

Mum and Dad demand respect,
They say that they're my betters.
But I can make them Dum and Mad
By changing round two letters.

Jaspre Bark

One-to-One

all my friends have
a mum and dad
or mum and stepdad
or dad and stepmum
or mum and her boyfriend
or dad and his girlfriend

I just have a dad
the best friend I've ever had

Lynne Taylor

Grounded

Grounded by Dad:
That's not too bad.
He says: "It's just the kind of trouble
I got into as a lad.
Of course, that doesn't mean
I can ignore it.
You must take your punishment,
I can't withdraw it.
But I'll reduce it from a week
To seven days (funny joke!).
No – three days. And tonight
We'll watch the match together
And I'll treat you to a coke."

Grounded by Mum:
That's grim, that's glum.
No Saturday match, no phone calls,
No pocket money;
No way she'll ever change her mind –
It isn't funny.
She goes on and on
And won't leave it.
She really means it.
You'd better believe it.

Eric Finney

Distant Relative

I'd rather
my father

were nearer

Dave Reeves

I Luv Me Mudder

I luv me mudder an me mudder luvs me
  We cum so far from over de sea,
We heard dat de streets were paved wid gold
  Sometimes it's hot, sometimes it's cold,
I luv me mudder an me muder luvs me
  We try fe live in harmony
Yu might know her as Valerie
  But to me she's just my mummy.

She shouts at me daddy so loud sometime
  She's always been a friend of mine
She's always doing de best she can
  She works so hard down ina Englan,
She's always singin sum kinda song
  She has big muscles an she very, very strong,
She likes pussycats and she luvs cashew nuts
  An she don't bother wid no if an buts.

I luv me mudder an me mudder luvs me
  We come so far from over de sea,
We heard dat de streets were paved wid gold
  Sometimes it's hot, sometimes it's cold,
I luv her and whatever we do
  Dis is a luv I know is true,
My people, I'm talking to yu
  Me an my mudder we luv yu too.

Benjamin Zephaniah

3

GRANDPARENTS
AND OTHER
RELATIVES

Grandad

You've been dead two years
but your cap sits on its peg,
pretending, like me.

I thought you'd come home.
Your hug in my dream last night
kept me warm all day.

Celia Gentles

My Gran

My gran is
    a giggle-in-the-corner-like-a-child
               kind of gran

She is
    a put-your-cold-hand-in-my-pocket
    a keep-your-baby-curls-in-my-locket
               kind of gran

She is
    a make-it-better-with-a-treacle-toffee
    a what-you-need's-a-cup-of-milky-coffee
    a hurry-home-I-love-you-awfully
               kind of gran

She is
    a butter-ball-for-your-bad-throat
    a stitch-your-doll-a-new-green-coat
    a let's-make-soapy-bubbles-float
    a hold-my-hand-I'm-seasick-in-a-boat
               kind of gran

She is
　　a toast-your-tootsies-by-the-fire
　　a crack-the-wishbone-for-your-heart's-desire
　　a ladies-don't-sweat-they-perspire
　　a funny-old-fashioned-higgledy-piggledy
　　-lady-to-admire
　　　　　　　　　kind of gran

And this lovely grandmother
　　is mine, all mine!

Moira Andrew

Grandpa

blossoms
out and up
over the weary waistband
of his trunks
(they must have seen
a hundred years of wear!)
knots his frayed hankie
like a parachute
to cover fraying hair
then eases down.

In less than half an hour
the Sunday Mail has slipped,
its rustle masking
Grandpa's gentle snore.
Sun and the journey,
age and the salt-sea air
return him to an earlier trip
(When I was young...)
The paper crumples,
slides to the sand
beneath his bulging chair.
Softly he sighs for summers lost;
snores loudly into sleep,
then settles dreams and flesh
more deeply in the canvas,
layer by layer.

Judith Nicholls

When Grandad was Young

'I had two pairs of shoes
(One for everyday and one for best)
The best ones only came out on Sundays
I would have to stuff my feet into them
Curl them up like fists 'til they burnt and hurt
    so much
That I'd end up walking to church on my hands

When I was young . . .
Vegetables were a luxury
Carrots were not all the same size
They were knobbly, covered in dirt
And resembled wizened old people
You didn't much like

When I was young . . .
You could have bread and butter
Or bread and jam – never both
Tangerines only appeared at Christmas
At the bottom of a very sweaty sock
With toenails in it.'

Lindsay McCrae

Marjorie

She was short-sighted and wore glasses.
She was a Sunday School teacher.
She was engaged to a soldier.
She had her picture taken in a grey dress.
She died at twenty-one of scarlet fever.
She was buried on Christmas Eve.
This is all I know about her,
The aunt I never knew, my mother's sister.
Is it my face or hers in the mirror?
Her face or mine in the frame?
And whom do they see when they look at me?

Sue Cowling

Long Lost Aunties

Aunties
Stretching out their
Octopus tentacles
Reeling me in for slobbering
Kisses.

John Coldwell

Family Album

I wish I liked Aunt Leonora
When she draws in her breath with a hiss
And with fingers of ice and a grip like a vice
She gives me a walloping kiss.

I wish I loved Uncle Nathaniel
(The one with the teeth and the snore).
He's really a pain when he tells me *again*
About what he did in the War.

I really don't care for Aunt Millie,
Her bangles and brooches and beads,
Or gun that she shoots or those ex-army boots
Or the terrible dogs that she breeds.

I simply can't stand Uncle Albert.
Quite frankly, he fills me with dread
When he gives us a tune with a knife, fork and spoon.
(I don't think he's right in the head.)

I wish I loved Hetty and Harry
(Aunt Hilary's horrible twins)
As they lie in their cots giving off lots and lots
Of gurgles and gargles and grins.

As for nieces or nephews or cousins
There seems nothing else one can do
Except sit in a chair and exchange a cold stare
As if we came out of a zoo.

Though they say blood is thicker than water,
I'm not at all certain it's so.
If you think it's the case, kindly write to this space.
It's something I'm anxious to know.

If we only could choose our relations
How happy, I'm certain, we'd be!
And just one thing more: I am perfectly sure
Mine all feel the same about me.

Charles Causley

My Grandma is a Nun

My grandma picks blackberries,
the plums and apples too,
she feeds the ducks
and feeds the hens,
she sees the morning dew
before she goes to say the prayers
for me, and you, and you.

She writes on her computer,
she reads great big thick books,
she makes the jam and chutney
and helps out other cooks.

At weekends she plans the menu,
picks parsley, chives and thyme,
my grandma is a fun nun,
and apart from God's, she's mine.

Chrissie Gittins

4
PLAYTIMES AT SCHOOL

Plague Around

There's a plague around
There's a plague around
In every village
And every town

With big purple spots
And greenish ones too
There's a plague around
And it's waiting for you

There's a plague around
There's a plague around
Keep your eyes open
And don't make a sound

Or your ears will flap
And you'll start to cough
You'll sneeze and sneeze
Till your nose drops off

There's a plague around
There's a plague around
In every school
There's a playground

You'll burst out laughing
And run around
When you get into
The playground

There's a playground
There's a playground
In every school
There's a playground.

Roger McGough

Chinese Whispers . . .

Jamie Delaney's got a spot on his nose
And a picture of batman tattooed on his toes.
Pass it on...
Johnnie McAllister's wearing girls clothes
And his hair is all set in ribbons and bows.
Pass it on...
I've heard our headmaster is daring and brave
He's been surfing the net on a crest of a wave.
Pass it on...
Pass it on faster before she turns round
Miss Murphy's got bats ears and hears every sound.
Pass it on...
I know who goes out with 'Rotten tooth' Ruth
Give us a sweet and I'll tell you the truth.
Pass it on...
Quick show me your answers before she asks me
You've done all of yours and I'm only on three.
Pass it on...

Diane Humphrey

Wet Play

Rainy windows,
Rainy faces,
Peering out at
Rainy places.

In the classroom
On a tray
Games that no-one
Wants to play.

Unkicked balls and
Unskipped ropes;
Unworn hats and
Gloves and coats.

Waiting for the
Wind to drop;
Waiting for the
Rain to stop.

Slowly it
Begins to clear.
Bright blue patches
Now appear.

Rainy clouds are
Blown away
And everyone
Goes out to play.

Marcus Parry

Playing Tennis with Justin

It's dinnertime and very sunny
I'm on the yard playing tennis with Justin.
Justin is winning fifty-five nil.

He's got a proper tennis bat called a rocket
I haven't got one so he gave me his spare one.
His rocket is filled up with string, mine isn't
Mine's got lots of holes.

If I hit the ball with the bit with no holes
It goes quite a long way, but usually
Justin says I've hit the net.

We haven't got a net but Justin says
He know where it would be
If we did have one.
Justin's very clever like that.

He's just scored fifteen more points
I nearly scored one a moment ago
But Justin said it was offside.
So the score is seventy-nil to him.

Justin says that my score is called love
Not nil, well I don't love it much
I keep losing, Justin says not to worry
I might score a six in a minute.

He says it's his second serve for juice
Well, the dinner lady hasn't called our group
In yet, so I haven't had one serving or any juice
I'm starving and it's very hot.

Justin says he's scored three more goals
And I should keep my eye on the ball
Then I might hit it with my rocket.

If Justin doesn't shut up quick
I might hit him with my rocket
I think tennis is rubbish.

Justin says we can play at cricket
But I've got to go in goals
Sometimes you just can't win
With Justin.

David Harmer

Teacher's Playtime

It's wonderful being on duty
When the teachers come out to play
See them running and shouting and leaping about
On a sunny winter's day

But I have to send Mr Walton
Back to the class for his coat
And Miss Atkins stayed in – there's a spot on her chin
(Her mother gave her a note)

Mrs Bateman hits Mr Fitton
She says he has stolen her ball
So I give her a lecture about sharing and caring
And I make her stand in the hall

Mrs Peck falls over and twists her foot
She's limping, but there's nothing to see
So I ask her to zoom to the staff room
To fetch me a cup of tea

Mr Owen is scared of Miss Pryor
He's hiding in the boy's bog
He says he'll stay there all day if she won't go away
'Cos she's trying to give him a snog

Mrs Rowlands, who works in the office,
Does a handstand against the wall
You can see her navy-blue knickers.
It's not very nice at all.

I love it on playground duty.
Bossing teachers still gives me a thrill.
So I ring the bell two minutes early.
And...

Mr Walton...

STAND STILL!

Roger Stevens (aged 10³/₄)

Sliding on the Ice

When weather's at its winterest
The game that grabs our interest
To leave us warm and feeling nice
Is sliding on the ice.
   To tell you once
   To tell you twice
   Is sliding on the ice.

So when the air is nippiest,
The frozen ground the slippiest
And tumbliest and trippiest
Then our idea of paradise
Is sliding on the ice.
   To tell you once
   To tell you twice
   Is sliding on the ice.

Yes, when our breath is cloudiest
The playground gets its rowdiest
Its loudliest and crowdiest.
The explanation, in a trice,
Is sliding on the ice.
   To tell you once
   To tell you twice
   Is sliding on the ice.

Nick Toczek

Playtimes

are for playing in,
racing round and chasing in,

calling, screaming, shouting out,
making friends and falling out,

tripping, slipping, kneecap scraping,
even arm and leg bone breaking,

bouncing, throwing, Frisbee flinging,
at the tops of voices, singing,

chalking risky words on walls,
in high gutters, losing balls,

playing football, passing, hogging,
hopscotch hopping, leapfrog frogging,

releaster, cricket with a stick,
dreading when the teams get picked,

"Fight! Fight!" crowding round,
two boys scrapping on the ground,

staying in when outside's wet,
teachers cross and kids upset,

if it's icy, sliding, skating,
under summer sunshine, baking,

cheeking some poor dinner lady,
holding Sally's mum's new baby,

losing coats, forgetting lunches,
older girls in giggling bunches –

but if you're new or on your own
there's no worse time to feel alone.

Trevor Parsons

New Boy

Out in the playground
Face like stone
Look at the new boy
   All alone.

New school uniform
Hair in place
Mummy's sweet kisses
Still wet on his face.

Poor little new boy
Filled with dread
Wishes he was home again
Safe in bed.

Gareth Owen

Talking to Mrs Thomas

'I'd rather not go into the playground, Mrs Thomas.
I've got a bad knee
and I may fall over
and make it badder.

If I could sit at the back
and read a book, or draw.
I'd be so quiet
you wouldn't know I was there.
...Well obviously if you looked up I would be there,
but if you didn't, look up that is, you wouldn't know I
was...there.

I'd rather not go into the playground, Mrs Thomas.
No, I don't think I'm trying to tell you something
but it looks like rain
and it will be such a bother
for you to send me out there
only to have to bring me back in again.
It hardly seems worth it.
So if I sit over by the radiator
and start drying off now
we'll be ahead of ourselves, won't we?
That would be quite good, wouldn't it?

I'd rather not go into the playground, Mrs Thomas.
No, nothing's frightening me much...
...My father said you've got to stand up for yourself
so that's quite good isn't it, Mrs Thomas?

You're going to the staff room to do some marking...
...can I come with you, please?

I'd rather not go into the playground, Mrs Thomas.
Please don't make me go into the playground,
Mrs Thomas.'

Stewart Henderson

Lets Shake on it

"Do you like football?"
"Yes I do."
"Do you want to be friends?"
"Yes I do."
"Ok let's shake on it!"
"Make friends, Make friends,
Never ever break friends!"
"Do you like Man U?"
"No I don't"
"Do you want to be friends?"
"No I don't"
"OK let's shake on it!"
"Break friends, Break friends,
Never ever make friends!"
"Do you still like me?"
"Yes I do."
"OK let's shake on it!"
"Make friends, Make friends,
Never ever break friends!"
"Do you mean it?"
"Yes I do!"

Jason Hulme

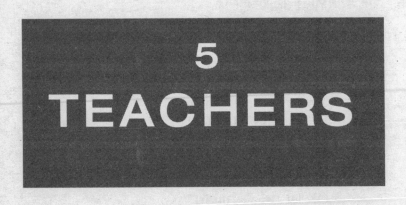

5
TEACHERS

The Teacher's Gift
(Margarette Nicholson, 1909-85)

Every time I tell the time
Or work out ten times two,
I open up a precious gift
Bequeathed to me by you.

You gave me names and numbers.
You taught me how to spell.
You told me how to hold a pen
And how to write as well.

You showed me how to read aloud
From books of red and blue.
You filled my head with goats and trolls
And tinderboxes too.

You planted seeds inside me
But did not see them grow.
A bell rings at the end of school
We pack our bags and go.

These words I scrawl on paper,
This shape upon my tongue,
Is made from things you gave to me
Way back when I was young.

Steve Turner

Cakes in the Staffroom

Nothing gets teachers more excited
than cakes in the staffrooom at break time.
Nothing gets them more delighted
than the sight of plates
piled high with jammy doughnuts
or chocolate cake

It's an absolute stampede
as the word gets round quickly,

And it's 'Oooh' these are really delicious
and 'Aaah' these doughnuts are ace.

And you hear them say, 'I really shouldn't'
or 'Just a tiny bit, I'm on a diet.'

Really, it's the only time they're quiet
when they're cramming cakes into their mouths,

when they're wearing a creamy moustache
or the jam squirts out like blood,
or they're licking chocolate
from their fingers.

You can tell when they've been scoffing,
they get languid in literacy,
sleepy in silent reading,
nonsensical in numeracy,
look guilty in assembly.

But nothing gets teachers more excited
than cakes in the staffroom at break time,
unless of course,
it's wine in the staffroom at lunch time!

Brian Moses

Miss Prim

Miss Prim
was tall and slim
and often pretended to be cross
to show us all that she was boss.

Anne Allinson

The Teacher

Here lies the teacher
who stayed in the warm
while his pupils were forced
to go out in the storm

While they were braving
the snow and the slush
the building collapsed
and the teacher was crushed

Andrea Shavick

Teacher

She's big and wide but moves just like a cat
Along a wall. She smiles like the queen.
Her choice of clothes is black. She wears a hat.
Although occasionally she will wear green.
She always marks your book in pencil, never pen.
Her voice is quiet. As quiet as falling snow.
She very rarely rages. Now and again
Her voice is raised. But does she shout? Oh no.
She fixes you with eyes as pale as snake.
She stops you dead. She sees into your soul.
You cannot move. Your heart beats and you shake.
You want to shout, I'm sorry. Let me go!
Her class will tell you that she's kind and fair.
They never misbehave. They wouldn't dare.

Roger Stevens

Skimpily Red

_____ and prim.

_____ chasing

I grinned at her. She put them back,
looked guilty as a thief.
I couldn't help but notice
they were very, very brief.

Her eyes met mine. She gave me such
a long hard icy stare,
and said 'Will Johnson! Why are you
in Ladies Underwear?'

As scarlet as those skimpy pants
I felt my face glow red.
Then mum looked up, peered round the stand.
'My son's with me,' she said.

Celia Gentles

Diving Lesson

Our sports teacher looked like an Olympic contender,
sleek as a dolphin piercing the water.

He barely made a splash when he dived in,
cutting the surface clean as a shark's fin.

Next he strode towards the high spring-board
stepped forward, bounced and up he soared

like an arrow above the sparkling blue
homing in, straight and true.

Then tucking up in a spinning ball,
He gobsmacked the crowd who watched his fall.

But he missed his timing, lost the plot.
He splashed down with a mighty belly-flop.

And things got worse, worse by a lot:
as he sunk to the bottom, his shorts floated up.

Stephen Clarke

Mr Flack

Our class has got a student,
His name is Mr Flack,
He wears a silver earring,
His hair is down his back.

He's very kind and friendly,
We know his name is Dave,
But sometimes it's too noisy,
And children won't behave.

He wears a Greenpeace T-shirt,
A cap and faded jeans,
He says he is a vegan,
And lives on runner beans.

He plays guitar in lessons,
And lets the class join in,
We clap and stamp in rhythm,
And make an awful din.

Miss Grant's a better teacher,
She's strict and keeps her cool,
But Mr Flack is funny,
And brightens up the school.

Tim Hopkins

Do You Know My Teacher?

(fill in the word you think is most appropriate)

She's got a piercing stare
and long black...

    a) teeth
    b) shoes
    c) moustache
    d) hair
    e) earlobes

She eats chips and beef
and has short sharp...

    a) doorstoppers
    b) fangs
    c) ears
    d) teef
    e) moonbeams

She is slinky and thin
and has a pointed...

    a) banana
    b) chin
    c) beard
    d) gorilla
    e) yacht

She has a very long nose
and hairy little...

    a) kneecaps
    b) paper clips
    c) children
    d) toes
    e) ornaments

She has sparkling eyes
and eats pork...

a) buses
b) ties
c) pies
d) thumbs
e) footballers

She comes from down south
and has a great big...

a) light bulb
b) eggcup
c) vocabulary
d) piano
e) mouth

She yells like a preacher
yes, that's my...

a) budgie
b) stick
c) padlock
d) duckling
e) teacher

John Rice

6
FRIENDS

A Good Play

We built a sip upon the stairs
All made of the back-bedroom chairs,
And filled it full of sofa pillows
To go a-sailing on the billows.

We took a saw and several nails,
And water in the nursery pails;
And Tom said, "Let us also take
An apple and a slice of cake;" –
Which was enough for Tom and me
To go a-sailing on, till tea.

We sailed along for days and days,
And had the very best of plays;
But Tom fell out and hurt his knee,
So there was no one left but me.

Robert Louis Stevenson

The Nothing Crew

We like doing nothing
and nothing's what we do.
By being good for nothing
is how our talent grew.
We hang around in precincts
and padlocked swing-parks, too,
we're ace at being nothing
'cos we're The Nothing Crew!

Well there's skateboard gangs
and Game Boys boys,
there's break-dance lads
making techno noise –
there goes a poser
on his racing bike –
well all that stuff
we don't like, 'cos...

We like doing nothing
and nothing's what we do.
By being good for nothing
is how our talent grew.
We hang around in precincts
and padlocked swing-parks, too,
we're ace at being nothing
'cos we're The Nothing Crew!

There's scratch card kids
out on the cadge
but, 'we have nothing'
is our badge.
Graffiti posse's
spray can touch
is never going
to grab us much.

Computer geeks
they make no sound
and some still have
a paper round,
and then there's
channel surfing nerds –
remote controlled
but lost for words

...'cos we like doing nothing
and nothing's what we do.
By being good for nothing
is how our talent grew.
We hang around in precincts
and padlocked swing-parks, too,
we're ace at being nothing
'cos we're The Nothing Crew...

Stewart Henderson

A Friend...

A friend is someone who borrows your ball
And returns it to you later in the day;
Who will lend their newest pens – and will play
Your games. Who'll come round to your house
  and call
For you in rain as well as when it's fine;
Who'll listen to your secrets, share your fears,
lend a shoulder when your eyes are full of tears
And won't divide things into 'yours' and 'mine'.
A friend will peel the plaster gently off your cut
And won't say 'Yuk!'. A friend laughs at your jokes
When others just go 'Eh?'; who likes you but
Will tell you when you're wrong; who strokes
Your favourite pet in spite of all the fleas –
Who knows your family but, when invited, says
  'Yes, please!'

Trevor Millum

A Friend's Prayer

Let me be the kind of friend,
Who's true and loyal to the end,
Who sees in the other all that's best
And tries to disregard the rest.

Teach me not to interrupt,
Or change the subject; be abrupt,
But listen with a patient ear
To all the things my friend holds dear.

Help me not to criticise
When they do things I think unwise,
But lend a hand if they should fall
And do not mention blame at all.

Let me be what I should prize
If I saw myself through another's eyes.
Lastly, I ask that I might be,
The kind of friend you've been to me.

Karen Costello-McFeat

Kidding Around

When I'm with Laura
     I need to be loud;
When I'm with Paula
     I always feel proud,
But when I'm with Carol
     I'm one of the crowd.

When I'm with Kevin
     I'm thoughtful and kind,
But when I'm with Michael
     I'm out of my mind.

When I'm with Wanda
     I want the last word;
When I'm with Bella
     I sing like a bird:
And when I'm with Hector
     I can hardly be heard.

But when I sit quietly
     Under this tree,
     This is the time
When I can be me.

Dave Ward

Jack

Jack
is my best friend,
I know I can trust him.
I don't have to win things
or prove that I'm strong.
When I'm in trouble
and nobody likes me,
I just call for Jack –
he's for me, right or wrong.

Jack
is my best friend,
who shares all my secrets.
My partner for ball games
and jumping off beds.
The last one I see
as I drift into sleeping,
and just as the pictures
of night fill my head ——

Jack licks my nose.

Daphne Kitching

Just Friends

Me and my friend
crawl through bushes to secret dens,
climb trees and walls,
play football.

My friend can flatten big boys with a shove
or stand like a rock and shout them down.
When we're together we're stronger than two
life's more fun with my friend around.

Me and my friend
don't have to pose or pretend:
there's nothing between us
but trust.

Yet the stupid sniggers are painful,
and silly gestures make me sore –
why can't a boy and girl be friends,
just friends, nothing more?

Dave Calder

Breaking the Rules

When Nadia started at our school
Miss said she should join our table,
But she didn't, she couldn't –
She sat with us, but apart,
Nobody let her in
That would be breaking the rules.
Friends have rules to keep others out,
To let them know they're not part of things.

Nadia had an accent,
It marked her out.
Lucy said, 'People with accents can't join us,
It's against the rules.'
Gemma said, 'People who aren't from round here
Have different rules.'

But on Saturday I saw Nadia in the park,
Pushing backwards and forwards on a swing,
Her feet still on the ground – with her heart.
When she saw me I noticed her melt into nothing.
Sorry seemed a small word.
'D'you want a push?' I asked.
Nadia smiled in a language I knew.
We spent all afternoon laughing and messing about
Breaking the rules.

Coral Rumble

A Boys' Song

Where the pools are bright and deep,
Where the grey trout lies asleep,
Up the river and over the lea,
That's the way for Billy and me.

Where the blackbird sings the latest,
Where the hawthorn blooms the sweetest,
Where the nestlings chirp and flee,
That's the way for Billy and me.

Where the mowers mow the cleanest,
Where the hay lies thick and greenest,
There to track the homeward bee,
That's the way for Billy and me.

Where the hazel bank is steepest,
Where the shadow falls the deepest,
Where the clustering nuts fall free,
That's the way for Billy and me.

This I know, I love to play,
Through the meadow, among the hay,
Up the water and over the lea,
That's the way for Billy and me.

James Hogg

Letter to My Best Friend

Dear Heather-Bell,

I was dead jealous of you,
what with your brown eyes
that shone like beads, your
pink dresses (to wear to school!)
your double-barrelled name.

You were a butterfly among
the blue gym slips. Miss Paterson
herself was bewitched. 'Watch
Heather-Bell.' she'd say. 'That's
how a little girl *should* behave.'

No matter that you poked out
your tongue behind her back.
You were never found out. I
tried it just once and was sent
to stand outside the door.

You had a magic, Heather-Bell.
When you asked me to sit by
you, I was in heaven. 'My best
best friend,' you said. But it
didn't last. Lucy was next.

Then Margery, Susan, Jane,
all the girls, one after another.
And we fell for it, your smile,
your dark curls, pink bow, the
best friend a girl could have.

With love from Rosie

PS. Your first best friend,
     Do you remember me?

Moira Andrew

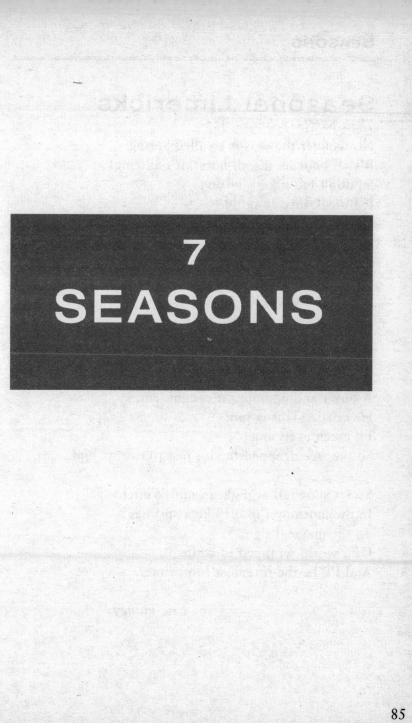

7
SEASONS

Seasonal Limericks

No wonder the season's called Spring:
It's all bounce, it's all burst, it's all zing!
So don't tell me it's wrong
If I break into song:
Hey, ding, ding-a-ling, dong-a-ling!

Summer picnics! Crisps, sandwiches, pop!
But the rain keeps on falling non-stop.
Say the kids, getting glummer,
"It's supposed to be Summer!"
Quite often the season's a flop.

A tree shed two leaves in the Autumn.
A boy standing under it caught 'em.
He cried, "This is fun!
I'll catch every one!"
So the tree dropped the lot just to thwart him.

Secret snowfall at night in mid-Winter.
In the morning I'm off like a sprinter
To the magical sight
Of a world wrapped in white
And I'll be the foremost footprinter.

Eric Finney

Frosted Flakes

Spring awakes
Summer bakes
Autumn shakes
But winter flakes

Andrea Shavick

12 Months Briefly

January freezy
February breezy
March snowy
April blowy
May's fine
June sunshine
July's just lovely all the time
August's great
September's cooling
October nights are damp and fooling
Miserable November's dreary
Hurray for December – nice and cheery.

Amanda Baxter

Seasons

A springtime tale
is best they say –
sunshine creeping in to play,
Easter tadpoles, beans in jars
birds in boxes
brand new cars.

A summer's tale
is ringed with flowers
cottage gardens, sunny hours
cotton dresses
cooing doves
summer sandals
summer loves.

An autumn tale you cannot see
it's not the sort of time for me –
fog and mist
long dark nights
soggy socks
woolly tights.

A winter's tale
is kissed with wine
frost and snuggles
logs and fires
carols, tinsel
warm deep beds
Christmas toys
and sleepy heads.

Peter Dixon

SPRING

A Change in the Year

It is the first mild day of March!
Each minute sweeter than before,
The redbreast sings from the tall larch
That stands beside our door.

There is a blessing in the air,
Which seems a sense of joy to yield
To the bare trees, and mountains bare,
And grass in the green field.

William Wordsworth

Spring

Nothing is so beautiful as spring –
When weeds, in wheels, shoot long and lovely
   and lush;
Thrush's eggs look little low heavens, and thrush
Through the echoing timber does so rinse and wring
The ear, it strikes like lightnings to hear him sing;
The glassy peartree leaves and blooms, they brush
The descending blue; that blue is all in a rush
With richness; the racing lambs too have fair
   their fling.

What is all this juice and all this joy?
A strain of the earth's sweet being in the beginning
In Eden garden. – Have, get, before it cloy,
Before it cloud, Christ, lord, and sour with sinning,
Innocent mind and Mayday in girl and boy,
Most, O maid's child, thy choice and worthy
   the winning.

Gerard Manley Hopkins

First Day of Spring

It's the first day of spring.

A girl and two boys
are mending a puncture.

The weak sun spikes the water
in the basin
and the bubbles from
the submerged inner tube
rise up like tiny balls.

Spanners, oil can, repair kit,
spoons and screwdrivers all lie
on the pavement,
warming their winter metal.

A girl and two boys
are mending a puncture
under a thin cloud,
beside nodding daffodils.

A new blue bike for a new yellow year.

John Rice

Spring Magic!

What a fearless magician is Spring –
you really can't teach her a thing!
In she sneaks on a breeze,
draws the leaves from their trees...
just when Winter thought he was still King!

Judith Nicholls

Spring

A newborn baby
cries. Listen, it is the sound
of winter dying.

Valerie Bloom

Spring Assembly

Right! As you all know,
It's spring pretty soon
And I want a real good one this year.
I want no slackers. I want SPRING!
That's S-P-R-I-N-G! Got it?
Spring! Jump! Leap!
Energy! Busting out all over!
Nothing so beautiful! Ding-a-ding-a-ding!

Flowers: I want a grand show from you –
Lot's of colour, lots of loveliness.

Daffodils: blow those gold trumpets.
Crocuses: poke up all over the parks and gardens,
Yellows, purples, whites; paint that picture.
And a nice show of blossom on the fruit trees.
Make it look like snow, just for a laugh,
Or loads of pink candy floss.

Winds: blow things about a bit.
North, South, East, West, get it all stirred up.
Get March nice and airy and exciting.

Rain: lots of shimmering showers please.
Soak the earth after its winter rest.
Water those seeds and seedlings.
And seeds: start pushing up.
Up! Up! Up! Let's see plenty of green.

Sunshine! give the earth a sparkle
After the rain. Warm things up.

And you birds: I haven't forgotten you.
Fill the gardens with song.
Build your nests (you'll remember how).
And you lambs: set an example,
Jump, leap, bound, bounce, spring!

And kids: ditch those coats and scarves,
And get running and skipping.
Use that playground, none of this
Hanging about by the school wall
With your hands in your jeans pockets.
It's spring, I tell you.
And you're part of it
And we've got to have a real good one this year.

Gerard Benson

A Date with Spring

Got a date with Spring
Got to look me best.
Of all the trees
I'll be the smartest dressed.

Perfumed breeze
behind me ear.
Pollen accessories
all in place.
Raindrop moisturizer
for me face.
Sunlight tints
to spruce up the hair.

What's the good of being a tree
if you can't flaunt your beauty?

Winter, I was naked.
Exposed as can be.
Me wardrobe took off
with the wind.
Life was a frosty slumber.
Now, Spring, here I come.
Can't wait to slip in
to me little green number.

John Agard

SUMMER

Summer

Rushes in a watery place,
> And reeds in a hollow;
A soaring skylark in the sky,
> A darting swallow;
And where pale blossom used to hang
> Ripe fruit to follow.

Christina Rossetti

Summer Haiku

Shimmering heat-waves –
A hot pebble in the hand,
Light-dance on the sea.

Wendy Cope

Summer Haikus

Flitting, fluttering,
weaving wild nothings, a pair
of whit butterflies!

Only just see him!
Titchy black dot. A skylark!
Listen, just listen!

Matt Simpson

The Hardest Thing to Do in the World

is stand in the hot sun
at the end of a long queue for ice creams
watching all the people who've just bought theirs
coming away from the queue
giving their ice creams their very first lick.

Michael Rosen

The Seaside Sand

The seaside sand in summer
Is crowded to the skies
With mums and dads and children,
With wasps and gulls and flies,
With ice creams and with sunshades,
With ships and stripy chairs,
With blow-up boats and beach balls,
With plastic shoes (in pairs),
With buckets and with castles,
With kites that swoop away,
With things that lurk in rock pools,
With donkeys chewing hay.

The seaside sand in winter
Is empty, but for me
And a line of doggy footprints
That scamper home for tea.

Clare Bevan

AUTUMN

Fall, Leaves, Fall

Fall, leaves, fall; die, flowers, away;
Lengthen night and shorten day;
Every leaf speaks bliss to me
Fluttering from the autumn tree.

I shall smile when wreaths of snow
Blossom where the rose should grow;
I shall sing when night's decay
Ushers in a drearier day.

Emily Brontë

No!

No sun – no moon!
No morn – no noon –
No dawn – no dusk – no proper time of day –
No sky – no earthly view –
No distance looking blue –
No road – no street – no 't'other side the way' –
No end to any Row –
No indications where the Crescents go –
No top to any steeple –
No recognitions of familiar people –
No courtesies for showing 'em –
No knowing 'em!
No travelling at all – no locomotion,
No inkling of the way – no notion –
'No go' – by land or ocean –
No mail – no post –
No news from any foreign coast –
No Park – no Ring – no afternoon gentility –
No company – no nobility –
No warmth, no cheerfulness, no healthful ease,
No comfortable feel in any member –
No shade, no shine, no butterflies, no bees,
No fruits, no flowers, no leaves, no birds –
November!

Thomas Hood

November Night

Listen...
With faint dry sound
Like steps of passing ghosts,
The leaves, frost-crisped, break from the trees
And fall.

Adelaide Crapsey

Autumn Rondelet

Under the trees
Wind blown branches litter the ground.
Under the trees
Racing, dancing, the season flees,
Summer gone, mist muffles all sound.
In shafts of light leaves twirl around
Under the trees.

Lucinda Jacob

Autumn

When I go out into the cold
I take my gloves and scarf and coat,
I pull on my boots and open the door,
And leave my mum a note.

When I go out into the cold
I go to the park to see the trees,
So big and brown, wearing a crown
Of glistening golden leaves.

When I go out into the cold
I see the ducks with downy feathers.
I walk along, up to the moor,
To see a field of wavering heathers.

After I've been out into the cold
I rush back home, where can be seen,
A little girl with a cup of hot chocolate,
Feasting on some jellybeans.

Yasamin Motamedi (aged 14)

Autumn Poem

litter
is
turning
brown
and
the
road
above
is
filled
with
hitch
hikers
heading
south

Roger McGough

Now my Green Days are all Done

I

t

w

i

s

t

And
Twizzle as I
Fall from above,
But have not the wide
Wings of a dove. No sweet
Beak to sing a song, my music is
Made by my feet as they march along –
And by the wild whoosh of the
Wind as it whirls and rustles
Me as it tussles me in its
Twirls. Now my green
Days are all done: I
Am red and gold
Like the sett-
Ing sun.

Tim Pointon

WINTER

Snow in the Suburbs

Every branch big with it,
Bent every twig with it;
Every fork like a white web-foot;
Every street and pavement mute:
Some flakes have lost their way, and grope back
    upward, when
Meeting those meandering down they turn and
    descend again.
The palings are glued together like a wall,
And there is no waft of win with the fleecy fall.

A sparrow enters the tree,
Whereon immediately
A snow-lump thrice his own slight size
Descends on him and showers his head and eyes,
And overturns him,
And near inurns him,
And lights on a nether twig, when its brush
Starts off a volley of other lodging lumps with a rush.

The steps are a blanched slope,
Up which, with feeble hope,
A black cat comes, wide-eyed and thin;
And we take him in.

Thomas Hardy

Winter Days

Icy fingers
Stinging toes
Ears tingle
Noses drip
One lost mitten.
Cold.

Radiators chatter
Duvet snuggle
Chocolate chuckles
Crispy toast
Butter dribbles
Hot.

Anne Wright

Winter

Winter is a...

Glove wearing
Scarf wrapping

Nose running
Lip chapping

Steam breathing
Water freezing

Frost biting
Nose sneezing

Snow falling
Grass crunching

Slip sliding
Hot lunching

Earth sleeping
    ...time of the year.

Damian Harvey

Long, Long Ago

Long, long ago
When winters were real
And snow was deep,
And woollen hats
And wellies
Were worn
By boys and girls,
My mum and dad
Used to take me
For walks –
Snow walks,
Cold walks,
White-frost-
On-the-breath walks.
With me, in between,
Holding their hands
And swinging with delight
And squealing with delight
So long long ago
When winters were real
And snow was deep
And childhood was mine.

Clive Webster

Winter

Drops an ice cube down my back
Then laughs with a cold shiver.

With a sniggery rush
It pushes a river of slush
From the roof to my neck.

Winter picks on me.

Jan Dean

8
CHRISTMAS

Merry Chrismix

Weather crackling.
Sleigh bells humming.
Vicar twinkling.
Robins praying.
Frost photographing.
Holly heating.
Slippers glowing.
Logs glinting.
Candles ringing.
Tinsel playing.
Angels snoring.
Santa baa-ing.
Music unwrapping.
Computers smiling.
Dogs dancing.
Stockings watching.
Presents visiting.
Dad crumbling.
Mince pies dangling.
Grandma barking.
Carol singers shining.
Mulled wine yawning.
Stars warming.
Shepherds hanging.
Sheep flying.
Biscuits raining.
Turkey singing.
Pudding hopping.
House burning.
Children cooking.

John Rice

The Christmas Rap

Christmas comin'
  buskers strummin'
  cash points hummin'
  high streets scrummin'
we're all of us succumbin' once again.
Christmas stockin'
  folks all flockin'
  debit cards dockin'
  loot unlockin'
like a bomb tick-tockin' in the drivin' rain.

We're Christmas rappin', yes we are.
  We're Christmas rappin', indeed we are.

Christmas buyin'
  very very tryin'
  lost kids cryin'
  debts multiplyin'
hotter than July in this department store.
Christmas shoppin'
  purses're poppin'
  rogues're robbin'
  aint no stoppin'
everyone's floppin' – can't take no more.

We're Christmas rappin', yes we are.
  We're Christmas rappin', indeed we are.

Christmas spendin'
  never ever endin'
  credit extendin'
  sharks out lendin'
tills all tendin' to overflow with cash.
Christmas wrappin'
  fivers flappin'
  plastic's snappin'
  your wallet's got a gap in
the shops are kidnappin' all of your stash.

We're Christmas rappin', yes we are.
  We're Christmas rappin', indeed we are.

Christmas queuin'
  cash machines chewin'
  big debts brewin'
  on the road to ruin
it's all just doin' mi 'ead in fast.
Christmas beginnin'
  Santa's grinnin'
  senses swimmin'
  wallets all slimmin'
and Slade blinkin' singin' – *It's CHRISTMAS!!*

We're Christmas rappin', yes we are.
  We're Christmas rappin', indeed we are.

David Horner

Saturday Night at the Bethlehem Arms

Very quiet really for a Saturday.
Just the old couple come to visit relations
Who took the double room above the yard
And were both of them in bed by half past nine.
Left me with that other one, the stranger.
Sat like he was set till Domesday at the corner of
   the bar
Sipping small beer dead slow and keeping mum,
Those beady, tax-collector's eyes of his
On my reflection in the glass behind the bar
Watching me, watching me.
And when he did get round to saying something
His talk was like those lines of gossamer
That fishermen send whispering across the water
To lure and hook unwary fish.
Not my type. And anyway I'd been on the go
   since five.
Dead beat I was.
Some of us have a bed to go to, I thought to myself.

I was just about to call Time
When the knock came at the door.
At first I was for turning them away;
We only have two rooms see and both of them were
   taken.

But something desperate in the woman's eyes
Made me think again and I told them,
They could rough it in the barn
If they didn't mind the cows and mules for company.
I know, I know. Soft, that's me.

I yawned, locked up, turned out the lights,
Rinsed my hands to lose the smell of beer.
Went up to bed.
A day like any other.
That's how it is.
Nothing much ever happen here.

Gareth Owen

Nativity in 20 Seconds

Silent night
Candle light
Holy bright

Stable poor
Prickly straw
Donkey snore

Babe asleep
Lambs leap
Shepherds peep

Star guide
Kings ride
Manger side

Angels wing
Bells ring
Children sing
WELCOME KING!

Coral Rumble

Christmas Wishes

A
star
shining,
angels singing,
snow shimmering,
two shepherds watching,
three proud kings travelling,
in a stable, a newborn baby crying,
in deep forests, silvery trees sparkling,
in high church towers, sweet bells chiming,
in busy streets, tinsel swaying, lights gleaming,
tambourines shaking, drums beating, trumpets blaring,
at home, mince pies baking, plum puddings steaming,
fat turkeys crackling, champagne bubbling,
the glad green tree, lights glistening,
Christmas greetings winging
across
frosty
winter
skies

Moira Andrew

Dear Santa

Dear Santa,
I'm a Dad who is deeply fed up.
I can hardly hold my head up.
I need this year, some real lifts,
Escapes from my usual dozens
Of hopelessly dozy gifts.

Christmas after Christmas
It's every year the same.
The family keeps playing
The same old, evil game.
Each year, at the present season,
They give me something worse
For which I must say: "Thank you."
(I can never, ever curse.)

I don't want to be a meany
I don't want to be a bore
I don't want to be an Oliver Twist
And ask my folks for more.

I just would like a single year
Without a pair of socks.
I do not want another shirt
That looks like Mother's frocks.

117

CHRISTMAS

I do not want more after-shave,
More slippers or more ties.
I do not want bright underpants
That dazzle my poor eyes.

I can't bear another dressing-gown.
I don't want another hat,
My drawers are full of handkerchiefs
And sweaters – stuff like that.

Dear Santa, if you love me,
If you really want to please,
Please bring me wine and chocolates
And different sorts of cheese.

I promise I'll be grateful
At tidings, oh so glad.
I'll never grouse or groan again,

Yours most sincerely,

Dad.

John Kitching

You at Christmas

You helped to mix the Christmas cake.
The stirring made your tired arms ache.

You hung the baubles on the tree
till it was glorious to see.

You set the crib out on the shelf
and put the baby in yourself.

You helped to hang the Christmas cards.
It seemed that there were yards and yards.

And, when it came to Christmas eve,
you whispered, "Yes, I do believe."

With great excitement in your head
you placed your stocking by your bed.

Then, switching off you bedroom light,
you turned to view the winter night.

And what you saw there caught your eyes
and made you startle with surprise.

No jolly Santa in his sleigh
with reindeer cantering away.

But just a star so silver bright
it seemed to fill the world with light.

And though so distant in the blue,
it hung and sparkled there for You.

Tony Mitton

Wrapping Christmas Parcels

Sello - strip
Sello - spin
Sello - scrumpled
Start again
Sello - sticky
Sello - stuck
Sello - sadly slanting, stuck
Sello - scrape off
Sello - scrap
Sello - try for better luck
Sello - smooth
Sello - round
Sello - end cannot be found
- except for torn off slither bit
Sello - slit
Sello - split
Sello - snap
Sello - tear
Sello - slide
Sello - slip
Sello - roll off under the chair

Try ribbon

Kate Williams

Bethlehem

Christmas is here again
in the streets and the shopping malls
in the pubs, the clubs and the churches,
in the tinsel hung school halls.

But in Bethlehem there's gunfire
on the streets of this holy place.
In the alleyways and the courtyards,
of Christmas there's little trace.

There's plenty of room at the inn tonight,
if Jesus came calling there,
but whose side would he support
in a battle on Manger Square.

Or would he stand between
terrorist and terrorized,
holding out hands and demanding
the violence be exorcised.

Or would he be mightily vexed
at the deeds of violent men.
For Jesus's sake let's bring Christmas
back to Bethlehem again.

Brian Moses

The Boxing Day Ghost

I am the ghost
of Boxing Day.

I live in broken presents
chucked away.

I live in all the turkey
not yet eaten;

in the crying children
my heart's beating.

I am the ghost
of Boxing Day

in the room full of relatives
with nothing to say

as Granny falls asleep
and Uncle spills his beer

my laugh is the thin, cold
sound you hear

and I'll be back
in another year:

the slob who lurks behind
the Christmas cheer.

Ian McMillan

9
BONFIRE NIGHT AND HALLOWE'EN

Bonfire Night Blues

Remember, remember,
The fifth of November,
Gunpowder, treason and plot.
Well, after last week's washout,
I would rather not.
My *Roman Candle* spluttered
And refused to light the sky.
My *Sparklers* wouldn't sparkle
And my *Rockets* wouldn't fly.
My *Bangers*, they just would not bang
And my *Golden Rain* went phutt!
My *Whizz-bang* blew out clouds of smoke
And covered me in soot.
My *Thunderflash* just fizzed a bit,
My *Crackers* wouldn't light.
My *Silver Fountain* whimpered –
It was such a sorry sight.
My *Jumping Jacks* declined to jump
And my *Catherine Wheels* to turn.
Not a single flipping firework worked,
Then the bonfire wouldn't burn.
I was feeling really cold and wet,
But when I began to groan,
My dad got really angry,
And he told me not to moan.
He said I was like a big damp squib
And then he sent me home.
So I don't want to remember Bonfire Night this year!

Gervase Phinn

Fireworks

Bang after bang tosses out
star and sunlit pieces
in a lit-up shower, drifting down.

In a slow party dance
meshed in bright shapes
of glowing lacework, like

necklaces, branches, arrows,
all drift down in
flame-pieces, rain-sparkled.

A fantastic Christmas tree of space
disappears before your eyes –
making you know the saddest goodbye.

James Berry

Trick or Treat

Trick or treat, trick or treat
Pumpkins light up every street
Trick or treat, trick or treat
Witches watch and gremlins greet
Trick or treat, trick or treat
Skeletons and vampires meet
Trick or trick or trick or treat

Hallowe'en, Hallowe'en
Ghost and ghouls, glowing green
Hallowe'en, Hallowe'en
Werewolves, hairy, scary, mean
Hallowe'en, Hallowe'en
Mummies lurch and monsters lean
Hallo Hallo Hallowe'en

Paul Cookson

Spinning

Catherine Wheel
spinning on a wooden post
like a galaxy,
but always in the middle
you can see there's a black hole.

Jill Townsend

Remember, Remember...

Laser Beam & Celebration,
Rainbow Blitz & Sonic Boom,
Atom Bomb & Pharoah's Candle,
Flashing Thunder, Dancing Moon

Butterflies & Wild White Orchids,
Jumping Jack & Crackling Fountain,
Raging Hailstorm, Roaring Lion,
Traffic Lights & Magic Mountain

Whistling Cake & Blooming Poppies,
Warlord, Starlight, Autumn Shower,
Radiant Moonbeam, Trailing Comet,
Asteroids & Budding Flower

Saxon Wheel & Breathing Dragon
Golden Harvest, U.F.O.,
Christmas Tree & Busy Bees
Silver Rain & Winter Snow –

Send them soaring, roaring upwards:
Light the flames and watch them fly.
Tonight's the night that every firework
Writes it's name upon the sky.

Graham Denton

Fireworks

Flames fly
Into the night,
Red and gold,
Effervescent and bright.
Watching children's
Oohs and Aahs, tell of
Rockets that zoom in
Kaleidoscope
Stars.

Celia Warren

A Cracking Day

The fifth
Of November,
However peacefully
It commences... always ends in
Fireworks!

Philip Waddell

Hallowe'en Hot-Pot

Blackhead of a greasy skin
in the cauldron simmering,
hair of nose and wax of ear,
scurf of scalp and salt of tear,
sticky eye and fur of tongue,
plaque of tooth and blood of gum.
For a spell stir at the double,
bring it to the boil
and bubble.

Gina Douthwaite

Trick or Treat?

Nervous, I hide upon my couch,
Not safe from harm on land or sea.
Crouched beneath my window-sill,
There is a child who wishes me ill.
I dare not stay. I dare not go.
I hear the cry of a jet-black crow
Perched high in the garden's leafless tree.
"What do you wish, dark child, of me
Now this trick-treat season has begun?"

This type of poem's a Telestich.
See the last letter of every line?
They'll spell out clear a word for you,
How many letters? Nine!

(Answer: Hallowe'en)

John Kitching

Fire at Night

It's ready steady sticks for fiery fun,
The strike of the match is the starter's gun.
Up go the flames, long-jumping sky,
The smoke catches up, hurdling high.
The crowd stamp their frozen feet
Clap their hands for the winning heat.
Guy Fawkes sits on top of the pyre,
Easily beaten, eaten by fire.
Who is quickest in the scorching race?
Flames of gold grab first place.
Who beat the day? The crowd then roars
The moon made silver to the stars applause.
Who has come third? No-one remembers,
As they all sprint home, leaving only bronze embers.
As clouds shuffle by with a marathon creep,
Children in bed clutch the prize of sleep.

Andrew Fusek Peters

Witch Villanelle

This night as I lie in my shadowed bed
I watch the moon in her cloudy shawls
And dream alone inside my head.

It's Hallowe'en when fear is spread,
My wide-awake ears hear screech-owl calls,
This night as I lie in my shadowed bed.

The clock strikes twelve, twelve chimes to dread.
I hear footsteps creak where a moonbeam falls
And dream alone inside my head.

I think I hear Moon-witches tread
And birch-horses stamp in their day-time stalls,
This night as I lie in my shadowed bed.

Far off to the dark wood the moon has fled.
I think of a tattered witch and trolls
And dream alone inside my head.

Though now from the sky no light is shed,
I see black cats leaping garden walls,
This night as I lie in my shadowed bed
And dream alone inside my head.

Catherine Benson

10
DIVALI
AND OTHER
FESTIVALS

Raksha Bandhan
(Brothers and Sisters Day)

Anhil, my brother, can be a real bossy-boots.
Sometimes we argue, sometimes we fight.
He wants this, and I want that,
And each of us always thinks we're right!

But at Raksha Bandhan
I will plait him a rakhi
Which I'll tie around his wrist
To keep him from harm.

He'll give me a present
And swear to look after me
(Last year he gave me
A tiny gold charm).

It's our special day to remember each other,
Fall-outs and fights don't matter, you see.
I know I really care about Anhil
And Anhil cares about me.

Patricia Leighton

The Naming Ceremony

Her name sounds like water, like waves on the sea,
like a summer breeze in the tallest tree.
  Ashanti, Ashanti, Ashanti.

Her dad is black, her mum is white.
They said, 'Please wear something bright.'
  For *Ashanti, Ashanti, Ashanti.*

We made a great circle under the sun.
Some poems were read, some songs were sung.
  To *Ashanti, Ashanti, Ashanti.*

We rattled our shakers, made music with bells.
A storyteller told tales, cast good African spells.
  Over Ashanti, Ashanti, Ashanti.

They blessed her, sprinkling her face with water,
said a prayer of thanks for their little daughter.
  Our Ashanti, Ashanti, Ashanti.

Her black grandfather then planted a tree.
Her white grandma held her up for all to see.
  Ashanti, Ashanti, Ashanti.

She was passed like a parcel in a party game,
as each whispered in turn her beautiful name.
  Ashanti, Ashanti, Ashanti.

Moira Andrew

Tuen Ng
(The Dragon Boat Races)

The air is hushed
round waiting boats;
water still before the race.
Slowly paddles lift
above the dragon-prows
like giant wing-bones
from a waking beast,
stretching into space...

And then...
they're off!
Away!

Fish scatter in dismay
as dragon-racers slice the surface.
Wings dip, whip water into waves;
waves rise like flames,
set light by sun.

Above, flags tug at their fetters,
desperate to join the fun.
And all around,
like pumping, thumping dragon-hearts,
the pounding gongs,
the beating drum.

Judith Nicholls

The Maypole
(May Day)

Alone on the green the Maypole stands,
    Its ribbons dangling down,
No longer the hub of the dancing girls
    Weaving their patterns around.

Alone on the green the Maypole stands,
    Tall and straight and proud
Though the music and laughter have died away
    And nothing is left of the crowd,

Alone on the green the Maypole stands,
    Queen of the May for tonight
The moon had clothed it in silver strands
    And crowned it with golden light.

Mal Lewis Jones

Shrove Tuesday

ceiling

I've got a funny feeling
that's my pancake, on the

Mike Johnson

Chinese New Year Dragon

There's a brightly coloured dragon swaying down
   the street,
Stomping and stamping and kicking up its feet.

There's a multicoloured dragon – green, gold and red –
Twisting and twirling and shaking its head.

There's a silky-scaled dragon parading through the town,
Swishing and swooshing and rippling up and down.

There's a swirling, whirling dragon, weaving to and fro,
Prancing and dancing and putting on a show.

There's cheering and clapping as the dragon draws near –
A sign of good luck and a happy new year!

John Foster

Rainbow Rice

When Arzana came to school today
She wore silky robes
That smelled of spices
And excitement.

She spoke of candle flames
And fireworks
That still sparkled in her eyes,
And she brought us bowls
Of rainbow-coloured rice
Tasting of sugar
And sweet surprises.

I shall forget the dates
Of kings and queens
And far-off battles.
I shall forget the names
Of tiny islands
In shimmering seas.
A thousand facts will slip from my mind
Like scuttling mice,

But years from now,
When I am no longer young
The tingle of Arzana's rainbow rice
Will always be
On the tip of my tongue.

Clare Bevan

Festival of Light

My first's in divine, but missing in light
My second's in justice and fairness and right
My third's in Ravana, a demon by name
My fourth is in lamp, and also in flame
My fifth's in rangoli, drawn on the floor
My last is in diva, the light at the door.

My whole is a time of great peace and joy
As we tell how Rama saved Sita, his wife.
Prayers for Lakshmi, the goddess, are said
As dancing and singing we celebrate life.

Angi Holden

Easter

When Jesus rode at Easter
into Jerusalem
a crowd cried out *Hosanna*!
I was one of them.

When Jesus prayed at Easter
in dark Gethsemane,
his friends all failed to stay awake –
I was of that company.

When Jesus stood at Easter
accused and put on trial
his friends all fled and turned away –
and I fled too – I ran a mile.

When Jesus died at Easter
The day the sky turned black ,
I wept at the sin and waste of it
and longed to bring him back.

When Jesus rose at Easter –
new life from death's cruel tree –
my heart broke with the joy of it
for this was done for me.

Jan Dean

It's Festival Time!

A festival! A festival!
A friendly, family festival.
The time of year that's best of all.

A festival! A festival!
Forget all things detestable
And dance in clothes majestical.
Your worries are divestistible.

A festival! A festival!
A friendly, family festival.
The time of year that's best of all.

A festival! A festival!
When food is most digestible,
And games are all contestable,
And presents are requestable.

A festival! A festival!
A friendly, family festival.
The time of year that's best of all.

A festival! A festival!
Sing songs and sound celestial.
Religions east and west have all
Got days they call a festival.

A festival! A festival!
A friendly, family festival.
The time of year that's best of all.
A festival! A festival!

Nick Toczek

11
ANIMALS
AND
BIRDS

The Fly

Little Fly,
Thy summer's play
My thoughtless hand
Has brushed away.

Am not I
A fly like thee?
Or art not thou
A man like me?

For I dance,
And drink, and sing,
Till some blind hand
Shall brush my wing.

If thought is life
And strength and breath,
And the want
Of thought is death;

Then am I
A happy fly,
If I live
Or if I die.

William Blake

Today I Saw the Dragon-Fly

Today I saw the dragon-fly
Come from the wells where he did lie.

An inner impulse rent the veil
Of his old husk: from head to tail
Came out clear plates of sapphire mail.
He dried his wings: like gauze they grew;
Through crofts and pastures wet with dew
A living flash of light he flew.

Alfred, Lord Tennyson

The Fallow Deer at the Lonely House

One without looks in to-night
    Through the curtain-chink
From the sheet of glistening white;
One without looks in to-night
    As we sit and think
    By the fender-brink.

We do not discern those eyes
    Watching in the snow;
Lit by lamps of rosy dyes
We do not discern those eyes
    Wondering, aglow,
    Fourfooted, tiptoe.

Thomas Hardy

Humming-Bird

I can imagine, in some other world
Primeval-dumb, far back
In that most awful stillness, that only gasped
   and hummed,
Humming-birds raced down the avenues.

Before anything had a soul,
While life was a heave of Matter, half inanimate,
This little bit chipped off in brilliance
And went whizzing through the slow, vast,
   succulent stems.

I believe there were no flowers then,
In the world where the humming-bird flashed ahead
   of creation.
I believe he pierced the slow vegetable veins with his
   long beak.
Probably he was big
As mosses, and little lizards, they say, were once big.
Probably he was a jabbing, terrifying monster.

We look at him through the wrong end of the long
   telescope of Time.

Luckily for us.

           D. H. Lawrence

Grasshoppers

Grasshoppers go in many a thrumming spring
And now to stalks of tasselled sour-grass cling,
That shakes and sways a while, but still keeps
    straight;
While arching oxeye doubles with his weight.
Next on the cat-tail grass with farther bound
He springs, that bends until they touch the ground.

John Clare

Minnows

Swarms of minnows show their little heads,
Staying their wavy bodies 'gainst the streams,
To taste the luxury of sunny beams
Tempered with coolness. How they ever wrestle
With their own sweet delight, and never nestle
Their silver bellies on the pebbly sand.
If you but scantily hold out the hand,
That very instant not one will remain;
But turn your eye, and they are there again.

from 'I stood tiptoe upon a little hill', *John Keats*

149

Coyote

Blown out of the prairie in twilight and dew,
Half bold and half timid, yet lazy all through;
Loth ever to leave, and yet fearful to stay,
He limps in the clearing, – an outcast in grey.

A shade on the stubble, a ghost by the wall,
Now leaping, now limping, now risking a fall,
Lop-eared and large-jointed, but ever always
A thoroughly vagabond outcast in grey.

Here, Carlo, old fellow, he's one of your kind, –
Go seek him, and bring him in out of the wind.
What! snarling, my Carlo! So – even dogs may
Deny their own kin in the outcast in grey.

Well, take what you will, – though it be on the sly,
Marauding or begging, – I shall not ask why;
But will call it a dole, just to help on his way
A four-footed friar in orders of grey!

Bret Harte

The Owl

From the faded rustlings of the night
comes the owl – wings outstretched in flight.
She takes her prey with taloned feet.
A loud hoot and cruel beak
the owl hunts before it's light.

Janis Priestley

Five Haiku for the Birds

Robin   Flashing your red badge
           You fix me with a bold eye:
           Christmas card hunchback.

Buzzard   There against the blue,
           A nonchalant skymaster
           Riding the thermals.

Wren   Wee bird, hardly seen –
           Just a flicker in the hedge.
           Jaunty though, that tail.

Goldfinch Such colours! You bring
           To a dull December day
           A tropical touch.

Rooks   High in wintry trees
           In cawing conversation:
           Swirling torn black rags.

Eric Finney

Life Sentence

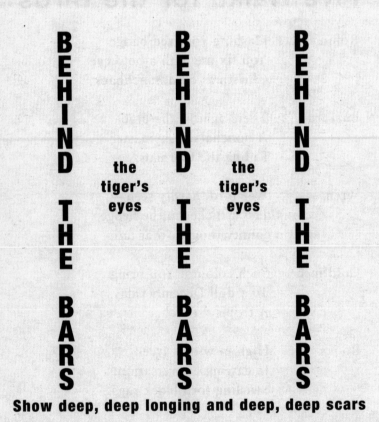

**B
E
H
I
N
D**

the
tiger's
eyes

**B
E
H
I
N
D**

the
tiger's
eyes

**B
E
H
I
N
D**

**T
H
E**

**T
H
E**

**T
H
E**

**B
A
R
S**

**B
A
R
S**

**B
A
R
S**

Show deep, deep longing and deep, deep scars

Coral Rumble

Fishes

Fishes
Tiny, shiny
Flashing, dashing, diving
Glimpses of ocean mystery
Teasers

Kate Williams

Old Mother Turtle

Slow thinker
eye blinker
tank on claws
wrinkled jaws
no bigger
sand digger
risk taker
egg layer
ambles off
does not watch
her tiny hatchlings
scrape, scuffle
hurry, shuffle
down to meet
the welcoming
waves.

Patricia Leighton

153

Bees Cannot Fly

Bees cannot fly, scientists have proved it.
It is all to do with wingspan and body-weight.
Aerodynamically incapable of sustained flight,
Bees simply cannot fly. And yet they do.

There's one there, unaware of its dodgy ratios,
A noisy bubble, a helium-filled steamroller.
Fat and proud of it, buzzing about the garden
As if it were the last day of the spring sales.

Trying on all the brightest flowers, squeezing itself
Into frilly numbers three sizes too small.
Bees can fly, there's no need to prove it. And sting.
When stung, do scientists refuse to believe it?

Roger McGough

Shire Horse

Stands so higH
Huge hooves toO
Impatiently waits foR
Reins and harnesS
Eager to leavE

Michael Lockwood

12
PETS

The Woodman's Dog

Shaggy, and lean, and shrewd, with pointed ears,
And tail cropped short, half lurcher and half cur –
His dog attends him. Close behind his heel
Now creeps he slow; and now, with many a frisk
Wide-scampering, snatches up the drifted snow
With ivory teeth, or ploughs it with his snout;
Then shakes his powdered coat, and barks for joy.

William Cowper

Living with Cats

The cat's shadow
stretches a thin dark rope
along the white wall.

And the shrew
snuffles the scent
through its long thin nose.

Know what it senses.

Goes jittering
skittering

a ping-pong ball
that wildly bounces

with not enough legs
to escape.

*

The balloon
like a fat pink pawprint
stuck on the sky.

The cats
stretch and yawn
in the tall grass.

Today they
do not care much about balloons
or hot air.

They are whispering
earthy sense to the mice

who twitch in their tunnels
just out of sight.

*

PETS

Next door's Spaniel
going ballistic

completely barking.

Cats in the sun
lazy as lions on the garage roof
wave their tails.

Next door's Spaniel
must be a springer

up and down
on his pogo-stick legs

howling and snarling
like a pack of bloodhounds.

Cats in the shade
half asleep on next door's patio
stick out their tongues.

*

Masie and Piglet
have tracked down the doormat
stalked the slidey, slippery rug
and pounced on the carpet.

Those jobs are done
no more trouble there.

Now they are watching the tropical fish tank
like some giant television
they are waiting for the channel to change
to their favourite programme

scuba diving for kittens.

*

Quickly and quietly
the cat crosses
the great green river
of the settee.

Paw to paw
avoiding the water
by delicate leaps

on the stepping stones
of our sleeping heads.

David Harmer

Ox and Axolotl

I had a little ox
And a little axolotl.
I liked my axolotl lots
I liked my ox a little.
My ox lived in a little box,
My axolotl in a bottle.
Box and bottle both lacked locks,
I lost my ox and axolotl.

Paul Bright

*An axolotl is a type of salamander, found mainly in
North America.*

Muuuuuuummmmmmm

Can we have a kitten
Can we have a dog
Can we call her Frisky
Can we call him Bob?
I can take him out each day
I can brush his fur
I will buy the dog meat
and milk to make her purrr
Mum!!!

Oh ... no ...
Well –

Can we have a donkey
or can we have a horse
a monkey or a parrot
hamster or a snake?
Can we have a guinea pig
a peahen
or a stoat,
llama or a budgie
a rabbit or a goat?

Can we have a crocodile
gibbon or an owl,
all the zoos are closing
there's lots and lots around...
A penguin would be really good
keep it in the bath
a hyena in the garden
    to make the milkman laugh.

No, WE DON'T WANT stick insects
and goldfish aren't much fun...

Oh, can we have a puppy...
    Mum
        Mum
            Muuuuuuummmmmmm.

Peter Dixon

Canary

The Dome of his head
Is round as an egg.
His skull as delicate as shell,
The bones inside his little body
Fine as pins.

I can spread his yellow wings
Like feather fans,
But he won't sing,
Not again. Not ever.
He is light as dust
And I must bury him.

His bright body
Like sunshine in a box
Deep in the shade
Of dark rhododendrons.
Muffled. Silent.
In the soft black soil.

Jan Dean

Pet Sounds

Flap rattle, claw scratch,
Purr in a sun patch,
Mad dash, tinkle ball,
Tuna crunch, chitter call,
Bag tear, carpet rip,
Sniff-sneeze at catnip,
Window tap, pane patter,
Oven leap, pan clatter,
Sleep-snuffle, dream-snore,
All these, and many more.

John Mole

Glitter

Glitter, my goldfish,
Blows bubbles for me – kisses
Round and wet and sweet.

Jennifer Curry

Call me Lucky

My human's smashing
He's really kind
And he spends all his time with me
He's a real leader

I talk to other dogs
They get left alone
Neglected sometimes
But my human
He's with me all the time
He shares his food
And even sleeps with me
We have a special doorway
And I keep him warm at nights
I'm such a lucky dog

Roger Stevens

Percy

I keep a secret in my room,
A pig called Percy.
He lives in a sty under the bed.
He's no trouble.
A bit noisy – Percy likes to dance a jig –
But he'll eat anything,
Old socks,
Orange peel,
School reports,
Dentist's appointments,
Greens.
He's especially handy when Mum's spring-cleaning,
Rooting around or being a busybody.
Although, last week I had a shock.
She called to me from the kitchen,
'Have you cleaned out that pigsty yet?'
She's no fool, my mother,
She might have heard Percy dancing.
So I've taught him the soft-shoe-shuffle.
As a precaution.

Mary Green

13
SPACE

Moonlight, Summer Moonlight

'Tis moonlight, summer moonlight,
All soft and still and fair;
The silent time of midnight
Shines sweetly everywhere,

But most where trees are sending
Their breezy boughs on high,
Or stooping low are lending
A shelter from the sky.

Emily Brontë

Space is Ace

Voice 1:
Space is ace
mysterious
above
beyond
around
the universe is singing
this huge, galactic sound
as Venus, Neptune, Jupiter
in three part harmony
read stars as crochets, quavers,
arranged by Mercury.

Voice 2:
Space is ace
astonishing
expanding
going on
to who knows where.
The later place?
The birth room of the Sun?
Up there
are many guesses
of untamed territory,
a stellar census we can't count,
a wild tranquillity.

Stewart Henderson

Information for Travellers

As you read this poem you are on a spacecraft
travelling at sixty six thousand miles an hour.
It spins as it flies: since you began to read
it has already turned nine miles to the east.
Be honest, you didn't feel a thing.
You are orbiting a star, not a very big one
compared to many of the ten thousand million others
that go round on the same galactic wheel,
and are flying at a height above its surface
of some ninety three million miles.
We hope to cruise at this distance for another
eight thousand million years. What happens then
is anybody's guess. Despite its speed and size
this craft is a spacestation, a satellite, not designed
for interstellar flight. Its passengers
rely on the comfort of a pressurised cabin
to enjoy the voyage. We must advise you that,
in the event of a collision, loss of atmosphere,
or any alteration in course which may result
in overheating or extreme cold, this craft is not
equipped with parachutes or emergency exits.
On a brighter note, the spaceship contains
an enormous variety of in-flight magazines,
meals to suit every taste, and enough
games, puzzles and adventures
to last a lifetime.
We hope you enjoy your voyage.
Thank you for flying Planet Earth.

Dave Calder

An Alphabet Trip Through Space

Astronauts in padded space-suits,
Booster rockets give us power,
Course is set for outer space
Docking carefully in an hour.

Engine revving, pushing onwards,
Fuel tanks full, some way to go.
Gravity is getting weaker,
Home is distant, far below.

Instruments show where we've got to,
Jetting through the Milky Way.
Kilometres measure distance,
Launch to lunar landing day.

Modules separate for landing,
Nitrogen is running low,
Oxygen feeds through the gas masks
Planets orbit, seem so slow.

Quick, it's time to go back home.
Radar tracks our tiny ship,
Satellites send on the signals
Transmitting every bleep and blip.

Unmanned rockets came before us
Vacuum sealed to be airtight.
Weightless, special cameras sent back
X-ray pictures through the night.

Year-long space trips, would be grand.
Zero hour, it's time to land.

Angi Holden

Achieving Liftoff –
in three stages

it
doesn't
matter how
much you
rehearse
it
how much you
practise
You're not a space
traveller until
the countdown's
ended
•

Astro   Ten
Astro   Nine
Astro   Eight
Astro   Seven
Astro   Six
Astro   Five
Astro   Four
Astro   Three
Astro   Two
Astro   One

Astro   naut
•

"We have liftoff!"
Astro naut
Astr o naut
Astr   o   naut
ooo
ooooo
o o o

Dave Reeves

Night Sky

Bright stars stud black skies.
Clear-seeing, we gaze amazed;
Winter-chilled but thrilled.
No wonder human beings
Seek to read the face of space.

John Kitching

Black Hole

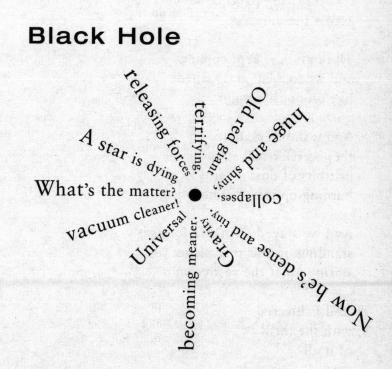

releasing forces
terrifying.
Old red giant
huge and shiny,
A star is dying
collapses.
What's the matter?
vacuum cleaner!
Universal
Now he's dense and tiny.
Gravity
becoming meaner.

Jane Clarke

The Shooting Stars

That night
we went out in the dark
and saw the shooting stars
was one of the best nights ever

It was as if someone
was throwing paint
across the universe

The stars just kept coming
and we 'oohed' and 'aahed'
like on bonfire night

And it didn't matter
they weren't real stars –
just bits of dust on fire
burning up in the atmosphere

And we stayed out there for ages
standing on this tiny planet
staring up at the vast cosmos

And I shivered
with the thrill
of it all

James Carter

Spaceship Earth

I am...

space-dancer,
drawn to the light like a moth;

an ancient coin
spun through night air;

silver penny,
lost in a deep pocket;

small change,
cast on a dark cloth –
a wager on life...

Spend me
if you dare!

Judith Nicholls

Moon Music

The Man in the Moon plays a tune
On a very old Silver Bassoon,
With a Thousand Guitars and a Chorus of Stars;
    And they sail in a Giant Balloon
        (Balloon)
    They sail in a Giant Balloon.

And the Music they make is so fine
It tickles and tingles your spine.
As they play up on high, they light up the sky.
    They sing as they play as they shine
        (They shine)
    They sing as they play as they shine.

And children tucked up in their beds
Hear that lovely old tune as it spreads
And the heavenly themes give them beautiful dreams,
    While the music sings on in their heads
        (Their heads)
    The music plays on in their heads.

With a Thousand Guitars on the tune,
And a wonderful Silver Bassoon,
The Music so grand fills the sea and the land
    When it's played by the Man in the Moon
        (The moon)
    When it's played by the Man in the Moon.

Gerard Benson

14
WEATHER

Morning After a Storm

There was a roaring in the wind all night;
The rain came heavily and fell in floods;
But now the sun is rising calm and bright;
The birds are singing in the distant woods;
Over his own sweet voice the stock-dove broods;
The Jay makes answer as the Magpie chatters;
And all the air is filled with pleasant noise of waters.

All things that love the sun are out of doors;
The sky rejoices in the morning's birth;
The grass is bright with rain-drops – on the moors
The hare is running races in her mirth;
And with her feet she from the plashy earth
Raises a mist, that, glittering in the sun,
Runs with her all the way, wherever she doth run.

William Wordsworth

Sunset

The summer sun is sinking low;
Only the tree-tops redden and glow;
Only the weather-cock on the spire
Of the village church is a flame of fire;
All is in shadow below.

Henry Wadsworth Longfellow

Thaw

Over the land freckled with snow half-thawed
The speculating rocks at their nests cawed
And saw from elm-tops, delicate as flower of grass,
What we below could not see, Winter pass.

Edward Thomas

Tornado!

Tree trunks, tables, tractors tossed like toys,
twizzled in the twister, tumbled, tattered
and tormented by the tearless tearaway,
the untamed tempest with a
tireless talent for turning
the terrain into a tapestry
of terror, as it twists
and turns, twists
and turns on
its tiny
terrible
tip!

Tim Pointon

Clouds

Shaping
of clouds by day
against the blue of sky –
strange images of creatures rise –
blending...

Moving,
they change their shape
then darken menacing,
foretelling heavy storms to come –
scaring...

Blowing,
they scud across
the black-cloth of that sky
What drama will unfold tonight?
Dreaming...

Joyce Goldsworth

The Whether Forecast

This is the whether forecast.
I don't know whether it'll rain or not.

Leo Aylen

Rainbows
(A Chaucerian Roundel)

Rich rainbows hoop the evening sky,
Defying bravely summer rain
That puddles field and leafy lane.

Delighting every young child's eye
For year on year, again, again,
Rich rainbows hoop the evening sky.

We need not ask the reason why
Their brightness eases heart-head pain.
While guttered rain drips into drain,
Rich raindrops hoop the evening sky.

John Kitching

Hot

It is hot.
So hot.

It is so hot,
Birds melt in flight,
Hot dogs get hotter,
Cats claw at each other's coats.

It is so hot,
Fish sweat,
Bodybuilders buckle,
Lollies lick themselves senseless,
And
Tee-shirts tan twice over.

It is so hot,
Beaches blanch
As
The scorched toes of the tide
Scamper retreat.

Simon Pitt

Snow Flurry

Snowflakes rushing,
Children hushing,
Corners fluffing –
Cotton-wooled.
People walking,
people stalking,
Slipping, sliding,
Being fooled.
Falling over,
Falling under,
Falling, falling
Down and down;
Making footprints,
Making handprints,
In the white tints
Of the town.

Coral Rumble

Take Two

A bruise of wind
fists the street;
a knuckle of rain
punches south.

The shutters bark
back and the moon
coughs discretely.

The fog busies itself
up some clipped alleyway.

Night nibbles dawn.

The stars lose control.

Pie Corbett

Snowball

More snow fell that week
than had fallen for thirty years.
The cold squeezed like a bully's hug
and made you grin at nothing.

Andrew Pond and Davy Rickers and me
went out,
three sprats,
into the white bite of the world.
We shared my balaclava.

And for an hour we chucked snowballs
at the windows on our estate;
spattered the pristine panes of Nelson Way,
powdered the gleaming glass up Churchill Drive,
until we got bored
and Andrew Pond's mitts from his granny
shrank.

It was me who started it off,
that last snowball,
rolling it from the size of a 50p scoop
down Thatcher Hill
to the size of a spacehopper.
It creaked under my gloves as I pushed.
Then Andrew Pond and Davy Rickers joined in,
and we shoved the thing
the length of Wellington Road.
It groaned as it grew
and grew.

The size of a sleeping polar bear.
The size of an igloo.
The size,
by the time we turned the corner
into the road where I lived,
of a full moon –
the three of us astronauts.

The worst of it was
that Andrew Pond and Davy Rickers ran off,
leaving me
dwarfed and alarmed
by a planet of snow
on our front lawn.
It went so dark in our living-room,
I was later to hear,
that my mother thought there had been an eclipse.

And later that night –
after the terrible telling-off,
red-eyed,
supperless –
I stared from my bedroom window
at the enormity of my crime,
huge and luminous
under the ice-cold stars.
To tell the truth,
it was pride I felt,
even though
I had to stop in for as long as it took
for the snowball to melt.

Carol Ann Duffy

Voices of Water

The water in the rain says *Tick Tick Tack*
The water in the sleet says *Slush*
The water in the ice says *Crick Crick Crack*
The water in the snow says *Hush*

The water in the sink says *Slosh Slosh*
The water in the tap says *Drip*
The water in the bath says *Wash Wash*
The water in the cup says *Sip*

The water in the pool says *Splish Splash*
The water in the stream says *Trill*
The water in the sea says *Crish Crash*
The water in the pond...stays still.

The water in the soil says *Sow Sow*
The water in the cloud says *Give*
The water in the plant says *Grow Grow*
The water in the world says *Live*

Tony Mitton

This is the Weather

This is the weather the vampire shuns,
And so do I;
When across the green meadow there clearly comes
A starling's cry;
And lakes brightly mirror the heaven's blue,
And cats under hedges the days slumber through,
And the monsters lie hidden from people like you...
And so do I.

This is the weather the vampire likes,
And so do I;
When lightning shivers its crooked spikes
Across the sky;
And a thunderous canonshot sunders the clouds,
And the dead deep in vaults softly stir in their shrouds,
And werefolk gather in whispering crowds...
And so do I.

Stephen Bowkett

Frost on the Flower

Frost on the flower,
Leaf and frond,
Snow on the field-path,
Ice on the pond.

Out of the east
A white wind comes.
Hail on the rooftop
Kettledrums.

Snow-fog wanders
Hollow and hill.
Along the valley
The stream is still.

Thunder and lightning.
Down slaps the rain.
No doubt about it.
Summer again.

Charles Causley

Snow

Things are often described,
'as white as' you.
You are very rarely
like something else.
And when you land,
and become spread out,
the streets go dense
with quiet.
It is as if you make us
listen and be glad.

When we roll in you,
scoop you up
and scatter you,
when we mound you
and build in you,
when we lie in you
on our backs
sweeping our arms
leaving the imprint of wings,
you do become something else –

because we imagine that angels
are shaped rather like us
but taller and glowing,
still with nostrils and ankles,
blowing bugles
and not getting told off,
and, obviously,
with wings.

But what if all along
it turned out
that you are an angel
bringing a message
of stillness
from a vast, pure place.

And when you melt
on pavements
and in fields,
what you are doing
is taking off,
but, in stages.

Maybe that is why
your rising
and disappearing
makes us so pray to you
from here below. . .
'...Don't go snow,
please don't go' . . .

Stewart Henderson

15
WATCHING
TELEVISION

Channels

Channel 1's no fun.
Channel 2's just news.
Channel 3's hard to see.
Channel 4 is just a bore.
Channel 5 is all jive.
Channel 6 needs to be fixed.
Channel 7 and Channel 8 –
Just old movies, not so great.
Channel 9's a waste of time.
Channel 10 is off, my child.
Wouldn't you like to *talk* awhile?

Shel Silverstein

The Girl on the News

Was my age,
liked the same music,
even had the same trainers.

Had a David Beckham shirt,
watched Coronation Street
and did Irish dancing.

Loved books by JK Rowling
and Jacqueline Wilson, had the full sets,
just like me.

For dinner she'd had a chicken sandwich,
crisps and a Mars bar ice cream.
I love them, they're my favourites too.

She loved the park... so do I,
in fact that was the last place anyone saw her
before she was...

If she'd been at my school
we would have been friends
best friends... definitely best friends.

But she won't now, missing for ten days
and even though nobody's said so we sort of know
there's not going to be a happy ending.

She was my age, just like me.
It could have been me that was taken.
I could have been the girl on the news.

She had the same colour eyes
and I was going to do my hair like that,
exactly like that...
but I don't think I will now,
I don't think I will now.

Paul Cookson

TV Rap

After school
what suits me
is to sit on the carpet
and watch TV.

Watch TV
Watch TV
I sit on the carpet
and watch TV.

I burst in
about half past three.
Kick off my shoes
and get comfy.

Get comfy
Get comfy
I kick off my shoes
and get comfy.

Dad says, 'You're too near.
Take my advice.
Move further back
or you'll damage your eyes.'

But my eyes don't hurt
and they haven't turned square.
Close to the screen
is what I prefer.

When I get home
what pleases me
is to sit on the carpet
and watch TV.
I watch TV
I watch TV
and I don't budge
until it's time for tea.

Time for tea
Time for tea
I don't budge
until it's time for tea.

Bernard Young

Watching TV

Every day you come home
You slump on the settee
You slurp a drink and eat some crisps
And then you stare at me

Well, I'm fed up being stared at
So this is what I'll do
I'm going to cancel all my programmes
And sit and stare at you

Roger Stevens

Widescreen

```
soapoperasneverstopmakeyoulaughorshockkeepyou
o                                            g
a                                            l
p                                            u
o                                            e
p                                            d
e                                            t
r                                            o
a                                            t
s                                            h
n                                            e
e                                            b
v                                            o
erstopmakeyoulaughorshockkeepyougluedtothebox
```

Mike Johnson

Boxed in

Surround-sound wide-screen DVD
Digital, terrestrial, MTV
Through square eyes is how I see
The remote control is controlling me

With my eyes on stalks and my brain in knots
I got glued to the gogglebox!

The only time I laugh is when I've Been Framed
Satellite dishes are replacing my brains
Quizzes, soaps and celebrity games
57 channels but they're all the same

With my eyes on stalks and my brain in knots
I got glued to the gogglebox!

TV dinner is all I ever eat
Teletubby life is sweeter than sweet
I record the best bits and press repeat
When I get told off I just delete

With my eyes on stalks and my brain in knots
I got glued to the gogglebox!

I push the button and I'm in the zone
I don't answer the door, I never pick up the phone
I watch every show that ever gets shown
With Ant and Dec I know I'm never alone

With my eyes on stalks and my brain in knots
I got glued to the gogglebox!

Steve Tasane

When My Dad Watches the News

When my dad watches the news...
You can start lots of fights
And swing from the lights,
You can throw all the cushions about,
You can smash every plate,
Keep on slamming the gate
And wear all you clothes inside out;
Do a dangerous trick
Or make yourself sick
By eating four packets of jelly,
You can 'prune' a few plants,
Donated by aunts,
Or draw Superman on his belly;
You can dig up the garden
Burp, and not say pardon,
Or write on the wall with a pen,
You can shout, "There's a fire!"
Or, "Mum's joined a choir!"
Or, "I'm leaving school when I'm ten!"
You can dance on the table,
For as long as you're able,
Then dive off the edge with real 'flair',
You can hair-gel the cat
So she's painful to pat,
You can staple your gran to the chair;
Phone a friend in New York,
And have a long talk,

Or tell him, "You've won a world cruise."
You can juggle with eggs
Or shave the dog's legs,
When my dad watches the news.

Coral Rumble

Television

This is what happens
Everytime I go in the
Lounge to
Enjoy some quiet
Video viewing.
In marches my big brother
Shouting
It's time for my favourite programme.
Out you go,
Now!

John Coldwell

After School

Switch on
Spiderman starts
I fight villains and win
Without stirring a fingertip.
Magic!

Angela Topping

The Day that the Telly Broke Down

It was worse than a hurricane, worse than a war,
Worse than a finger that's stuck in the door,
Worse than the worst ever worst thing before

THE DAY THAT THE TELLY BROKE DOWN

My brother attempted to give it first aid.
We told it we loved it, its licence was paid.
We cried and we whimpered, we knelt down and
  prayed

THE DAY THAT THE TELLY BROKE DOWN

Our mum said, 'Don't worry, there's homework to do
Or something creative with glitter and glue
And just for a treat there's some washing-up too!'

THE DAY THAT THE TELLY BROKE DOWN

We could help with the ironing, go out for a walk,
Teach the parrot to do something other than squawk
Or do as they did in the olden days – talk!

THE DAY THAT THE TELLY BROKE DOWN

We considered the options with infinite care:
Like buy a new telly, attempt a repair
Or sit in our rooms wailing, 'Life's so unfair!'

THE DAY THAT THE TELLY BROKE DOWN

Instead we decided to visit our aunt
'Lend us your telly.' She said ''Fraid I can't.
This morning your uncle thought it was a plant
(and watered it!) so . . .
I'M AFRAID THAT THE TELLY HAS DROWNED

Lindsay McCrae

A Televised Surprise

Imagine our delight
Consternation and surprise
Our teacher on *Come Dancing*
Right before our eyes.

She wore a dress of sequins
That glittered like a flight
Of silent, silver snowflakes
On a winter's night.

She really looked fantastic
No one could ignore
The magic of her dancing
Across the ballroom floor.

Her partner, tall and smart
Only saw him from the back,
Oily hair slicked down short
His suit and shoes were black.

He whirled and twirled her round
As the music got much faster
And then he faced the camera
It was our headmaster!

They seemed to dance for ever
Having so much fun
And then the competition stopped
The pair of them had won.

David Harmer

16
MYTHICAL BEASTS

The Kraken

Below the thunders of the upper deep;
Far far beneath in the abysmal sea,
His ancient, dreamless, uninvaded sleep
The Kraken sleepeth: faintest sunlights flee
About his shadowy sides: above him swell
Huge sponges of millennial growth and height;
And far away into the sickly light,
From many a wondrous grot and secret cell
Unnumber'd and enormous polypi
Winnow with giant fins the slumbering green.
There hath he lain for ages and will lie
Battening upon huge seaworms in his sleep,
Until the latter fire shall heat the deep;
Then once by men and angels to be seen,
In roaring he shall rise and on the surface die.

Alfred, Lord Tennyson

Leviathan

Canst thou draw out leviathan with an hook?
Or his tongue with a cord which thou lettest down?
Canst thou put an hook into his nose?
Or bore his jaw through with a thorn? . . .
Who can open the doors of his face?
His teeth are terrible round about.
His scales are his pride,
Shut up together as with a close seal . . .
Out of his mouth go burning lamps,
And sparks of fire leap out.
Out of his nostrils goeth smoke,
As out of a seething pot or cauldron.
His breath kindleth coals,
And a flame goeth out of his mouth . . .
He maketh the deep to boil like a pot:
He maketh the sea like a pot of ointment.
He maketh a path to shine after him;
One would think the deep to be hoary.
Upon earth there is not his like,
Who is made without fear.
He beholdeth all high things:
He is a king over all the children of pride.

Book of Job, The Bible

The Dragon

There's a dragon in our garden
That hatched out under the shed,
Her scales are shaped like teardrops
And glow when she's been fed.

She sleeps all through the daytime,
Wings folded like a bat,
Gold and green and dreaming
And purring like a cat.

But she's getting wild and restless
So she'll fly away quite soon
To the only place
Where a dragon's still safe:
Deep inside the moon.

Kevin McCann

Yeti

He's in the Himalayas, yeti
      hasn't been found,
He leaves us great big footprints, yeti
      doesn't make a sound,
He doesn't live on garlic bread
      or meatballs, or spaghetti –
There's nothing there to eat, yeti
      does, yeti does.

He's never been measured, yeti's
      seven metres tall
He lives in snowy places, yeti
      can't get cold at all
His abominable woman
      is the kind you can't forget, he
Could be getting married yeti
      won't, yeti won't.

He is a sort of snowman, yeti
      won't melt in the sun
A kind of 'I don't know' man, yeti's
      definitely one
Or maybe only half a man,
      don't know, we haven't met, he
isn't really real yeti
      is, yeti is.

Ros Barber

Together Ness

Bashful Ness,
Timid Ness,
Coy Ness,
Shy Ness.
Address?
Loch Ness.

Philip Waddell

The Ballad of Unicorn Isle

Once upon a faraway time
Before the clocks had learned to chime
When every river spoke in rhyme
Once upon a time

Once within a distant land
Where mountains hadn't heard of man
Where dolphins played and bluebirds sang
Once within a land

Then and there in echoing light
Where gold was day and silver night
Lived unicorns of purest black and white
There in echoing light

One shining day in shimmering glade
The seer had come to speak they said
An ancient one with eyes of jade
One shimmering shining day

"I saw the future far away –
Hearken friends to what I say!
I saw grey night and I saw grey day
In the future far away!

I saw the pale two legged beast
Rise up from west, rise up from east
And slay our kind for fun and feast
The pale two-legged beast.

It hunted down the unicorn
It cut off head, it cut off horn
Or stole our foals as they were born
And caged the noble unicorn"

Once upon a desperate hour
In the shadow of the great moonflower
They made a pact to use their power
Upon a desperate hour.

So faded they from human sight
Though wild geese see them from their flight
And children dream of them at night
Invisible to human sight

Once within a faraway land
Where unicorns first heard of man
Where hotels rise and tourists tan
Once within a land...

Trevor Millum

The Mermaid and the Fisherman

By a cave of coral the mermaid sits
Beneath a silvery moon
And the lonely fisherman hears her voice
As she sings a haunting tune.

He forgets his nets and he grabs the oars
And he swings the boat around
To head for the shore for he must hear more
Of the soft bewitching sound.

By a cave of coral the mermaid smiles
Hearing the splash of an oar
And the grating of pebbles on the beach
As a boat is pulled ashore.

The fisherman stands in front of the cave
With a wild look in his eyes.
On a seaweed bed in a coral cave
An enchanting mermaid lies.

The fisherman reaches out with his hand
To touch her silvery hair
And the mermaid smiles as she lures him down
To capture him in her lair.

In a coral cave a fisherman sits,
Spellbound at a mermaid's side.
On the beach above an abandoned boat
Is lapped by the morning tide.

John Foster

The Song of the Wicked Giant

I'm a hairy, scary Giant
With a Giant's hairy chest
And I crunch the bones of girls and boys,
But it's boys I love the best.
For boys are prawns and curry
With a whiff of dirty feet,
But girls are rose and lavender
And MUSH TOO SWEET!

aaaaaaaaaaaaaaargh!

Fee Fi Fo Fum
I EAT your Dad and I EAT you mum!
I EAT all the fluffy bits out of my tum!
Fee Fi Fo Fum

There's Giants, Troll and Ogres
With Axes, Clubs and Knives,
And we're all extremely practised
At taking children's lives.
We turn you into meatballs
And boil you in a stew
Which is yummyish and flavoursome
And MADE OF YOU!

aaaaaaaaaaaaaaargh!

Fee Fi Fo Fum!
I can WIGGLE my ears while I SCRATCH my bum!
You OPEN the cupboard and OUT I COME!
Fee Fi Fo Fum!

John Whitworth

213

Magical Beast

Beast of beauty, wise and bold
Fabled horse with horn of gold
Said to live where rainbows end
Graceful, gentle fairies' friend
Golden mane and golden tail
Magic hoofs that leave no trail
Only visible it seems
In children's minds at night in dreams.

(Or is it? Can you spot the magical beast?)

Richard Caley

17
FOOD

Ode to Chips

Chips, chips, wonderful chips:
Just say the word and my lid nearly flips.
When you're passing the chip-shop, man, the waft,
It's delicious enough to drive you daft!
As a meal, or between meals, you simply can't whack it,
So why don't you purchase a piping hot packet?
Gorgeously gold, shading gently to brown,
They're best from The Friendly Frier in town.

Chips, chips, marvellous chips:
They haven't got bones and they haven't got pips,
And you don't need a knife or a fork – it's just blissful:
You just stick in your hand and come up with a fistful.
You can scoff 'em – I tell you there's no handicaps –
Right down to those last little nutty brown scraps.
When you've done, and you're licking the taste from
your lips,
And you're thinking of afters ...well, what about chips?

Chips, chips, magnificent chips –
I'm just going to leave you a few final tips:
Some like 'em with bangers, some like 'em with curry
(Though later they may find themselves in a hurry),
Some like 'em with eggs and some like to poke
The ends of their chips in the warm, yellow yolk.
As for me (just excuse me for licking my lips),
I just like 'em with more and more mountains of chips.

Eric Finney

My Mum
(for Chris)

Calls it
Spaceman's Relish
And she
Zaps it
In a blender
Drowns it
In gravy
Mashes it
With potatoes
Hides it
Under chips
Scatters it
With sweetcorn
Nukes it
In the microwave
And follows it
With ice-cream

But
It's
Still
Cabbage!

Kevin McCann

Pizza Pizza

O pizza pizza margherita,
My favourite, my fiery wheel,
O piece of pizza, can I eat ya,
Can I have you every meal?

Squelchy, spicy, chewy ring
Of tomato, cheese and creamy dough,
Golden honey-crusted heaven,
Warm sea of goo – I love you so!

Your glowing red and yellow sun
Melting, and I lick my lips
As you slide over the moon of my plate
Making a total eclipse!

So feast of pizza, piece of pizza,
Nothing beats yer inner glow,
When I meets yer, I must eats yer,
The thrill, the frill, the hill of dough.

Taste, the final frontier,
In my sky of pizza, look at this!
Planets of mushroom, pepper, pepperoni,
Extra toppings, extra bliss.

O pizza pizza margherita,
How I wonder what's for tea,
O stuffed crust in the sky above
I hope you're big enough for me.

Matt Black

Chopsticks

```
                    C
   C                h
   h                o
   o                p
   p                s
   s                t
   t                i
   i                c
   c                k
   k                s
   s
```

Chicken   chow   mein
Prawn crackers. Spring rolls.
Take away again.
Char sui. Chop suey.
Egg fried rice.
Chinese food
is very nice.

Catharine Boddy

The Rev Spooner's Shopping List

Jaspberry ram
Chot hocolate
Ninger guts
Beggie vurger
Sea poup
Spixed mice
Lairy fiquid
Bea tags
Pushroom mizza
Chini meddars
Jackcurrant belly
Poo laper
Nicken choodles
Haghetti spoops
Lire fighters
Glubber roves
Sup a coup
Poothtaste
Palf a hound of Chensleydale wheese
and
Baked beans
(Gank thoodness)

Andy Seed

Jelly-lover

Jill likes stuff that wobbles, quivers,
Trembles and gives little shivers,
Ripples, promising rich pleasure,
Glitters like Aladdin's treasure,
Green or red or orange, yellow,
Sharp and fruity, sweet and mellow.
Jill likes jelly in the belly,
She would eat it from a welly;
Loves to see it shake and shudder,
Brightly joggle, jounce and judder.
She adores its slippery motion
And could wallow in an ocean,
Not of green and foamy briny
But lime jelly, smooth and shiny.
Jill, whose best friend calls her Jilly,
Said, 'I hope I don't sound silly
If I say my dream vacation
Has to be an invitation
To an island, gold and shining,
Where I'd spend all day reclining
By a sprinkling sherbet fountain
Shaded by a jelly mountain.'

Vernon Scannell

The Food that gets stuck in the Plug of the Sink

A soggy tomato
  and yesterday's peas,
a dried up sultana,
  a lump of green cheese!

It's juicy, it's fruity,
  it's green and it's pink.
The food that get stuck
  in the plug of the sink.

Mushrooms and meatballs,
  a pineapple chunk,
a fried egg and gravy,
  a sausage that sunk!

It's juicy, it's fruity,
  it's green and it's pink.
The food that gets stuck
  in the plug of the sink.

Teabags and spinach,
  bananas and beans,
some pasta and peelings,
  a pig's intestines!

It's juicy, it's fruity,
  it's green and it's pink.
The food that gets stuck
  in the plug of the sink.

John Rice

Mr Khan's Shop

is dark and beautiful.
There are parathas,

garam masala,
nan breads full of fruit.

Shiny emerald chillies
lie like incendiary bombs.

There are bhindi in sacks,
aloo to eat with hot puris

and mango pickle. There's
rice, yoghurt,

cucumber and mint –
raitha to cool the tongue.

Sometimes you see
where the shop darkens

Mr Khan, his wife
and their children

round the table.
The smells have come alive.

He serves me
puppadums, smiles,

re-enters the dark.
Perhaps one day

he'll ask me to dine with them:
bhajees, samosas, pakoras,

coriander, dhall.
I'll give him this poem: *Sit down*

young man, he'll say
and eat your words.

                    Fred Sedgwick

Rap Up My Lunch

This is the lunchtime slip slop rap
Spaghetti hoops or sausage in a bap
Click your fingers, stamp your feet
Groovy gravy, two veg, no meat,
Shake your body, swivel those hips,
Salt and vinegar, fish and chips
Hold your hands up in the air
Chocolate custard, apple or pear
Feel that beat, you're on the loose
Lemonade or orange juice,
Chatter clatter, make a noise
No more hungry girls and boys
Rhythm and rap to the roasting rhyme,
Lunch is done, it's playtime.

Andrew Fusek Peters

I Cannot Fight It

I cannot fight it.
Like a wave the craving comes.
Must have chocolate!

Ted Scheu

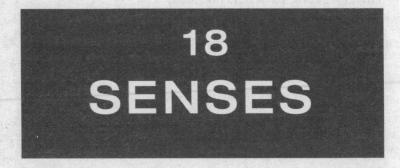

18
SENSES

Senses

I see the brown creosoted wood of the shed,
The grey stone path beneath me,
Long grass in front of me, short behind.

I hear a blackbirds's song and a robin's chirrup,
A church bell in the distance,
The clunk and chug of my motor.

I feel sharp twigs beneath my roller,
The teasing tickle of soft stubble
And the warm moist palm of my master's guiding hand.

I smell sweet honeysuckle,
The pungent stink of compost,
And onion gravy through an open window.

I taste salt sweat on my handles,
Sweet sap from the cut stems
And the meaty savour of minced worm.

What am I?

Mick Gowar

The Sixth Sense

Mum has baked a cake.
I can smell it from my bedroom.
I shall follow my nose to the kitchen.
Aah, a sight for sore eyes.
Not that mine are sore;
they are keen, all too keen.
So, it's butter icing is it.
My taste buds are tingling.
I am salivating like Pavlov's dog.
My fingers creep towards the icing.
Nothing can beat the velvety texture
of sweet, sweet icing,
the feeling as the finger plunges in and...
Aaargh! Mum. You needn't shout like that.
It was just a quick lick.
I think my eardrums have burst.
By the way, we did the five senses today at school
and I have just used all mine.
It was an educational exercise
so I would have thought
that you would have been pleased.
I have returned to my room to sulk.
There is a sixth sense too, you know.
They don't mention it at school of course
but it is telling me at this very minute
that I shall not be getting any cake.

Marian Swinger

228

Give Thanks

Thanks for my eyes
Which give me sight
Of colours, shape and form.
The sunset in the evening.
The brilliance of the morn.

Thanks for my ears
Which give me sounds
Of laughter, music, talk.
The waves upon the sea-shore.
Leaves rustle as I walk.

Thanks for my nose
Which gives me scents
Of new mown grass and rain.
The bacon sizzling in the pan.
The flowers in the lane.

Thanks for my mouth
Which gives me taste
Of all things sour and sweet.
Of apple pie and ice-cream
Delicious things to eat.

Thanks for my hands
Which give me touch
Of roughness or of smooth.
Of coldest snow or warmest sands.
And gentle strokes to soothe.

But most of all
My sense of me
Of who I am, and want to be.
For loving thoughts and caring acts.
I give my thanks for me!

Brenda Williams

Nonsense Poem

This poem sees nothing.
It hears nothing.
It tastes and smells nothing.
It touches nothing.
This is a non-sense poem.

Nick Toczek

Senses

This is the sea
It tastes like salt

This is salt
It feels like sand

This is sand
It smells like the sea

This is the sea
It sounds like the wind

This is the wind
For all to see.

This is the snow
It looks like wool

This is wool
It feels like a blanket

This is a blanket
It sounds like my sister

This is my sister
She smells like warm milk

This is cold milk
It tastes like the snow

John Turner

Look With Your Eyes

"Look with your eyes
And not with your fingers."
That's what my grandma
Used to say.

And my brothers and I
Used to say to each other:
"Listen with your nose.
Smell with your toes.
Or if that's too boring,
Look at that music
And taste that drawing.
Hasn't it got a lovely scent?"

But, really, you know,
We knew what she meant.

Gerard Benson

The Oldest Girl in the World

Children, I remember how I could hear
with my soft young ears
the tiny sounds of the air –
tinkles and chimes
like minuscule bells
ringing continually there;
clinks and chinks
like glasses of sparky gooseberry wine,
jolly and glinting and raised in the air.
Yes, I could hear like a bat. And how!
Can't hear a sniff of it now.

Truly, believe me, I could all the time see
every insect that crawled in a bush,
every bird that hid in a tree,
individually.
If I wanted to catch a caterpillar
to keep as a pet in a box
I had only to watch a cabbage
and there it would be,
crawling bendy and green towards me.
Yes, I could see with the eyes of a cat. Miaow!
Can't see a sniff of it now.

And my sense of taste was second to none.
By God, the amount I knew with my tongue!
The shrewd taste of a walnut's brain.
The taste of a train from a bridge.
Of a kiss. Of air chewy with midge.
Of fudge from a factory two miles away
from the house where I lived.
I'd stick out my tongue
to savour the sky in a droplet of rain.
Yes, I could taste like the fang of a snake. Wow!
Can't taste a sniff of it now.

On the scent, what couldn't I smell
with my delicate nose, my nostrils of pearl?
I could smell the world!
Snow. Soot. Soil.
Satsumas snug in their Christmas sock.
The ink of pen.
The stink of an elephant's skin.
The blue broth of a swimming-pool. Dive in!
The showbizzy gasp of the wind.
Yes, I could smell like a copper's dog. Bow-wow!
Can't smell a sniff of it now.

As for my sense of touch
it was too much!
The cold of a snowball
felt through the vanishing heat of a mitt.
A peach like an apple wearing a vest.
The raffia dish of a bird's nest.
A hot chestnut
branding the palm at the heart of the fist.
The stab of the thorn on the rose. Long grass, its itch.
Yes, I could feel with the sensitive hand of a ghost.
   Whooo!
Can't feel a sniff of it now.

Can't see a
Can't hear a
Can't taste a
Can't smell a
Can't feel a bit of it whiff of it niff of it.
Can't get a sniff of it now.

       Carol Ann Duffy

SMELL

Heaven Scent

I love the smell
of fish and chips
candy floss
and
cherry lips

curried beef
basmati rice
oranges
and
nutmeg spice

jammy donuts
chewing gum
my baby sister
and
my mum

bags of popcorn
at the fair
and me
when I've just washed my hair

Celia Gentles

The Smell of Melon

the smell of melon –
wondering
if it's ripe

Katherine Gallagher

There was...

A horrible smell in the hallway,
A terrible stink up the stair,
A dreadful stench on the landing,
A stink-bomb pong in the air,

A particularly nasty aroma,
An odour to make you feel sick,
A pong to punish your nostrils,
A smell all putrid and thick.

It was as gross as rotted bananas,
As foul as the corpse of that rat
In the cupboard underneath the stairs
Once brought in by the cat.

I rushed out into the garden,
I made it pretty snappy!
Mummy was up in the bedroom, yuck,
Changing the baby's nappy!

Matt Simpson

Wouldn't it be Funny if You Didn't Have a Nose?

You couldn't smell your dinner
If you didn't have a nose
You couldn't tell a dirty nappy
From a summer rose
You couldn't smell the ocean
Or the traffic, I suppose
Oh wouldn't it be funny
If you didn't have a nose?

You couldn't smell your mummy
If you didn't have a nose
You couldn't tell an orange
From a row of smelly toes
You couldn't smell the burning
(Think how quick a fire grows)
Wouldn't it be funny
If you didn't have a nose?

Where would we be without our hooters
Nothing else would really suit us.
What would we sniff through?
How would we sneeze?
What would we wipe
Upon our sleeves?

You couldn't smell a rat
If you didn't have a nose
You couldn't tell a duchess
From a herd of buffaloes
And...mmmm that Gorgonzola
As it starts to decompose
Oh wouldn't it be funny
If you didn't have a nose?

Where would we be without our hooters?
Nothing else would really suit us.
And think of those who
Rub their noses
Life would be tough for
Eskimoses

You couldn't wear your glasses
If you didn't have a nose
And what would bullies aim for
When it came to blows?
Where would nostrils be without them?
When it's runny how it glows
Oh wouldn't it be funny
If you didn't have a...

        have a...
        have a...
            a...
            a...
            a... choo!

Roger McGough

TASTE

Chocolate

Sound of expectant silence, anticipating pleasureS
Eyes light up at the first glimpsE
Nostrils flare to drink the aroma iN
Sensually smooth surface to stroke with fingertipS
Eagerly anticipating the first all-encompassing tastE
Senses tingle as the first touch on the tongue explodeS

Susan Bates

Sunshine Breakfast

Granny haggle fe ortaniques
From de higgler dung de market.
She pick a firm fruit
Tek a sharp knife
Slice off de rind,
Right dung to de flesh
Careful, oh so careful.
Den, she prong
De golden orb onto de fork,
Smile, and give it me.
Den I suck, suck, suck,
All de juice from de orange lollipop.

Anita Marie Sackett

*Ortaniques are a cross between an orange and
a tangerine
A higgler is a vendor*

Raspberries

The taste of the first raspberries is my grandmother's
back garden – three-quarters crazy paving, mossed
and crumbling, split with weeds, and leading to
the yew-lined arbour like an open stage.
Old roses hang across a broken trellis,
creepers on the high white wall; bees
throng between them and the flowers
and fruit canes packed against a neighbour's fence.
Out of the kitchen smells of metal polish,
cakes and jam, an old lop-sided spaniel
slowly flaps along the path to savour
   her last days of sun.

Tony Lucas

Chocolate Cake

I love chocolate cake.
And when I was a boy
I loved it even more.

Sometimes we used to have it for tea
and Mum used to say,
'If there's any left over
you can have it to take to school
tomorrow to have at playtime.'
And the next day I would take it to school

wrapped up in tin foil
open it up at playtime
and sit in the corner of the playground
eating it,
you know how the icing on top
is all shiny and it cracks as you
bite into it,
and there's that other kind of icing in
the middle
and it sticks to your hands and you
can lick your fingers
and lick your lips
oh it's lovely.
yeah.

Anyway,
once we had this chocolate cake for tea
and later I went to bed
but while I was in bed
I found myself waking up
licking my lips
and smiling.
I woke up proper.
'The chocolate cake.'
It was the first thing I thought of.

I could almost see it
so I thought,
what if I go downstairs
and have a little nibble, yeah?

It was all dark
everyone was in bed
so it must have been really late
but I got out of bed,
crept out of the door

there's always a creaky floorboard, isn't there?

Past Mum and Dad's room,
careful not to tread on bits of broken toys
or bits of Lego
you know what it's like treading on Lego
with your bare feet,

yowwww
shhhhhhh

downstairs
into the kitchen
open the cupboard
and there it is
all shining.

So I take it out of the cupboard
put it on the table
and I see that
there's a few crumbs lying about on the plate,
so I lick my finger and run my finger all over the
    crumbs
scooping them up
and put them into my mouth.

oooooooommmmmmmm

nice.

Then
I look again
and on one side where it's been cut,
it's all crumbly.

So I take a knife
I think I'll just tidy that up a bit,
cut off the crumbly bits
scoop them all up
and into the mouth

0000000mmm mmmm
nice.

Look at the cake again.

That looks a bit funny now,
one side doesn't match the other
I'll just even it up a bit, eh?

Take the knife
and slice.
This time the knife makes a little cracky noise
as it goes through the hard icing on top.

A whole slice this time,

into the mouth.

Oh the icing on top
and the icing in the middle
ohhhhhh oooo mmmmmm.

But now
I can't stop myself
Knife –
I just take any old slice at it
and I've got this great big chunk
and I'm cramming it in
what a greedy pig
but it's so nice,

and there's another
and another and I'm squealing and I'm smacking my
  lips
and I'm stuffing myself with it
and
before I know
I've eaten the lot.
The whole lot.

I look at the plate.
It's all gone.

Oh no
they're bound to notice, aren't they,
a whole chocolate cake doesn't just disappear
does it?

What shall I do?

I know. I'll wash the plate up,
and the knife

and put them away and maybe no one
will notice, eh?

So I do that
and creep creep creep
back to bed
into bed
doze off
licking my lips
with a lovely feeling in my belly.
Mmmmmmmmmm.

In the morning I get up,
downstairs,
have breakfast,
Mum's saying,
'Have you got your dinner money?'
and I say,
'Yes.'
'And don't forget to take some chocolate cake with
    you.'
I stopped breathing.

'What's the matter,' she says,
'you normally jump at chocolate cake?'

I'm still not breathing,
and she's looking very closely now.

She's looking at me just below my mouth.
'What's that?' she says.
'What's what?' I say.

'What's that there?'
'Where?'
'There,' she says, pointing at my chin.
'I don't know,' I say.

'It looks like chocolate,' she says.
'It's not chocolate is it?'
No answer.
'Is it?'
'I don't know.'
She goes to the cupboard
looks in, up, top, middle, bottom,
turns back to me.
'It's gone.
It's gone.
You haven't eaten it, have you?'
'I don't know.'
'You don't know. You don't know if you've eaten a
    whole
chocolate cake or not?
When? When did you eat it?'

So I told her,

and she said
well what could she say?

'That's the last time I give you any cake to take
to school.
Now go. Get out
no wait
not before you've washed your dirty sticky face.'
I went upstairs
looked in the mirror
and there it was,
just below my mouth,
a chocolate smudge.
The give-away.
Maybe she'll forget about it by next week.

Michael Rosen

SIGHT

The Colours in God's Paintbox

If I wasn't me
I'd like to be a colour from God's paint box.

Maybe a green that would shade
a thousand different leaves
on a thousand different trees,
the green that causes emeralds to shine,
the glint in a kitten's eyes,
the liquid freshness of the oean
or the lush moistness of the rainforest.

Possibly a blue,
whether the pastel, peaceful sky,
the splash on the wing of a Jay,
the deep sea calmness,
the paleness of a blackbird's eggshell
or the electric flash of storms.

The red slash of poppyfields,
the thickened shades of blood,
the crimson sheen of appleskin,
the petals on a rosebush
or the setting sun at eventide.

A million shades of blue
and a millions shades of green,
a million shades of every hue
and a million in between.

Colours clash then melt together
in God's Royal Flush
then drip in perfect shades
from His one and only brush.

Paul Cookson

Eyes on the Time

When I travel in a train
and I want other passengers
to look at their watches

I get my mum and dad
to mumble something to themselves
a little loudly, then look
at their watches with a purpose.

Then I just sit back pop-eyed
counting how many people do
look at their watches.

James Berry

The Colour Collector

A stranger called this morning
Dressed all in back and grey
Put every colour into a bag
And carried them away

The goldness of cornflakes
The ivory of milk
The silverness of soupspoons
The see-throughness of silk

The greenness of tennis-courts
When play had just begun
The orangeness of oranges
Glowing in the sun

The blueness of a dolphin
Nosing through the sea
The redness of a robin
Breasting in the tree

The creaminess of polar bears
Sliding on the floes
The little piggy pinkness
Of tiny, tickly toes,

The sky that smiled a rainbow
Now wears a leaden frown
Who's sobbing in his caravan?
Wizzo the monochrome clown

A stranger called this morning
He didn't leave his name
We live now in the shadows
Life will never be the same.

Roger McGough

Periscope

It's as simple as this –

light enters, strikes **an angled mirror**

dives down a tube, hits

an angled mirror **and flies on into the eye**

the delighted eye of a tiny child
watching a procession
over the heads of the crowd,
the cold eye of a submarine captain,
snug under the waves,
sighting the packed troopship,
finger tense above a red button.

It's as simple as that.

Trevor Parsons

Roll Cameras

Two eyes,
twin directors,
scan the scene before them,
making film for memory. That's
a wrap!

Karen Costello-McFeat

SOUND

Night Sounds

The hoot of an owl
The purr of a car
The thud of a door
The scratch of a key
The click of a lock
The groan of a door
The scuff of a shoe
The creak of the stair
The groan of the hall
The swing of the door
The whisper of draught
The shuffle of shoe
The shiver of breath
The rustle of clothes
The kiss of a kiss
The silence of sleep

Roger Stevens

Listen Here

Bring your shell – like over here – I've got a

secret.

Can you hear?

Jill Townsend

SSHH!

Quiet as the daytime creeping in,
Or someone dropping a tiny pin

Quiet as a painting starting to dry,
Or the footsteps of a walking fly

Quiet as a glider soaring in the sky,
Or the lashes fluttering across your eye

Quiet as an owl swooping in the night,
Or a beautiful butterfly's very first flight

Quiet as a memory, a sorrow, a fear,
Or a wonderful dream, right inside here

Quietness is precious, so seek it out,
But when you find it...please don't SHOUT!

Les Baynton

The Sound Collector

A stranger called this morning
Dressed all in black and grey
Put every sound into a bag
And carried them away

The whistling of the kettle
The turning of the lock
The purring of the kitten
The ticking of the clock

The popping of the toaster
The crunching of the flakes
When you spread the marmalade
The scraping noise it makes

The hissing of the frying-pan
The ticking of the grill
The bubbling of the bathtub
As it starts to fill

The drumming of the raindrops
On the window-pane
When you do the washing-up
The gurgle of the drain

The crying of the baby
The squeaking of the chair
The swishing of the curtain
The creaking of the stair

A stranger called this morning
He didn't leave his name
Left us only silence
Life will never be the same.

Roger McGough

The Bells

Hear the sledges with the bells –
Silver bells!
What a world of merriment their melody foretells!
How they tinkle, tinkle, tinkle,
In an icy air of night!
While the starts that oversprinkle
All the heavens, seem to twinkle
With a crystalline delight;
Keeping time, time, time,
In a sort of Runic rhyme,
To the tintinnabulation that so musically wells
From the bells, bells, bells, bells,
Bells, bells, bells –
From the jingling and the tinkling of bells.

Edgar Allan Poe

TOUCH

Touch

To feel
A snowflake melt
On the tip of your tongue,
Shows you how sacred the gift of
Touch is.

Jaspre Bark

I Can See You Now

When I first met
My blind friend Grace
She said, "Will you please let me
Touch your face?"

I felt her gentle hands
Upon my skin:
She felt my lips and eyebrows
Then my nose and cheeks and chin.

Last of all she felt my hair
And gently held my head
Then with a lovely smile:
"I can see you now," she said.

Eric Finney

These are the Hands

These are the hands that wave
These are the hands that clap
These are the hands that pray
These are the hands that tap

These are the hands that grip
These are the hands that write
These are the hands that paint
These are the hands that fight

These are the hands that hug
These are the hands that squeeze
These are the hands that point
These are the hands that tease

These are the hands that fix
These are the hands that mend
These are the hands that give
These are the hands that lend

These are the hands that take
These are the hands that poke
These are the hands that heal
These are the hands that stroke

These are the hands that hold
These are the hands that love
These are the hands of mine
That fit me like a glove

Paul Cookson

19
HOLIDAYS

Holiday Rap

We're going away, we're going away,
we're going away on holiday

to climb up rocks and abseil down
miles in the hills away from town,
to try canoeing over rapids,
sleep beneath a bivouac, it's
great when centipedes and ants
invade your sleeping bag and pants,

we're going away, we're going away,
we're gong away on holiday

to capsize yachts upon the sea,
ride mountain bikes and dri-slope ski,
try air ballooning – what a gas
to sail above a vast crevasse,
and pony trek across the hills
till sitting in the saddle *kills*,

we're going away, we're going away,
we're going away on holiday

to try a shot at archery –
a bull for you, a calf for me,
to crawl in caves deep underground
where muddy waters slop around
and blackness wraps your eyes – and hands
slap clammy cavern walls. It's grand!

We're going away, we're going away,
we're going away on holiday

to orienteer with compasses,
use O.S maps, get lost in mists
where lakes have swallowed '*Rights of Way*'
so off the beaten track we'll stray
to swing like spiders right across
a gaping gorge. We've flipped because
we're going away,
        we're going away,
                we're going away ...

Gina Douthwaite

Beach Umbrella

You'll find that you'll lack it, if you forget to pack it

E
ssential on a summer
beach, when sun is bright enough
to bleach, for – as fierce rays are blazing down
– it controls the rate that you go brown: no matter
where the sunlight glows, adjust the height, its shadow
grows. Protects your eyes from stress or strain – and
comes
in
ha
nd
yw
he
ni
ts
ta
rt
st
or
ai
n,
ag
ai
n!

Mike Johnson

Packing and Unpacking

Suitcase yawns... a happy hippo waiting to be fed.
Let's tuck fresh folded food deep into his mouth!
Watch him gulp underwear and sweaters,
swallow toys and books.
Hungry still? We'll press in trousers,
socks and swimsuits,
shorts, towels and trainers,
add frocks and silver sandals for dessert.

Hippo groans. It's been a long day.
Twist the key and spring the locks.
Crumpled clothes froth.
Small hands burrow for pebbles in a bag,
sticks of rock, a box of shells.
Linen basket fills as Hippo slims,
and dreams of meals to come.

Shirley Tomlinson

Miss You

Midbay-on-Sea
August 10th

Dear Kevin
        Just a line from here –
Miss you, miss you, miss you, dear!
Both sea and sky down here are grey;
So far its rained all holiday –
Looks like going on for weeks.
Our caravan has fifteen leaks:
It's saturated all our gear.
Kevin, love, wish you were here.
Dad says the beer down here's no good.
The beach has got no sand – just mud;
And what's between us and the sea?
You'll never guess – a cemetery.
My new swimsuit gave Mum a fit:
She says there's not enough of it.
(I'm pretty sure you won't agree:
It does show off a lot of me!)
If you were here to joke and natter
The gloom and doom just wouldn't matter.
Coming with them it's pretty clear,
Was not a brilliant idea.
Closing now, Kev, I'm off to bed;
Think I've got flu, I feel half-dead.

Hoping from this exciting whirl
You're not out with some other girl.
Miss you at Misery-on-Sea,
Love you to bits.

Your girlfriend,
G

Eric Finney

A Riddle to Pack in Your Suitcase

My 1st is in wishing and also in hope,
My 2nd's in towel and also in soap,
My 3rd is in sleep and also in lie,
My 4th is in fruit and also in pie,
My 5th is in day but also in dark,
My 6th is in boat and also in ark,
My 7th's in yes but also in nay,
My whole is a time to relax and play.

Celia Warren

(Answer: holiday)

Seaside Song

It was a
sun-boiled, bright light, fried egg, hot skin, sun-
tanned
ssssizzzzzzler of a day.

It was a
pop song, ding-dong, candy floss, dodgem car, arcade,
no shade
smashing seaside town.

We had
a well time, a swell time, a real pell-mell time,
a fine time, a rhyme time, a super double-dime time.

We
beach swam, ate ham, gobbled up a chicken leg,
climbed trees, chased bees,
got stuck in sand up to our knees,
played chase, flew in space,
beat a seagull in a skating race,
rowed boats, quenched throats,
spent a load of £5 notes,
sang songs, hummed tunes,
played hide and seek in sandy dunes.

Did all these things
too much by far
that we fell asleep going back in the car
from the seaside.

John Rice

Bank Holiday

Far beyond the dingy pier,
The derricks and the dirty boats,
Water waves her ringlets, floats
In crystal cleanliness, cool, clear,
Calm and collected. As for us, we're
Sweating on this beach, our coats
Stretched out beside us, and our throats
As tight as terror, stiff as fear.

Oh for a coke, a ginger pop,
To touch our tongues, to lick our lips,
But all we do all day is flop
And long for breezy, tousled trips
Across the sea or dream one drop
That drips and drips and drips and drips.

John Mole

Ways to Get into the Pool
– Instructions for Parents

starfish
bellyflop
scissors jump
dive
sitting jump
knee-hug
woosh! down the slide
backwards roly-poly,
but if you're over 35

...use the steps!

Andrea Shavick

Poem to Read While you Wait

Wait at the bus stop.
Wait in the rain.
Wait on the journey to
   Wait for the train.
Wait while it takes you to
Wait for your plane.
Wait at the flight gate.
Wait there in vain.
Wait and wait and wait and wait
And wait and wait again.

Wait at the help desk.
Wait to complain.
Wait while the staff there
Wait to explain.
Wait with your passport.
Wait but remain.
Wait till the waiting
Drives you insane.
Wait and wait and wait and wait
And wait and wait again.

Wait on the tarmac.
Wait on the plane.
Wait while the plane's weight
Takes the flight lane.
Wait for a could break.
Wait to see terrain.
Wait while you circle.
Wait to land again.
Wait and wait and wait and wait
And wait and wait again.

Wait in the gangway
Waiting to deplane.
Wait for your suitcase.
Waiting is a pain.
Wait with a headache.
Wait while your brain
Waits to see if waiting
Triggers your migraine.
Wait and wait and wait and wait
And wait and wait again.

Nick Toczek

Traffic Jam

We started early
And travelled far
But now we're sick
Of being in the car

Traffic jam
Traffic jam
We're stuck in a traffic jam

When we set off
Six hours ago
We never imagined
We'd feel this low

Traffic jam
Traffic jam
We're stuck in a traffic jam

Mum is grumbling
Dad is growling
My brother's moaning
I feel like howling

Traffic jam
Traffic jam
We're stuck in a traffic jam

I fear I'll grow old
And my hair will be grey
By the time we begin
Our holiday

Traffic jam
Traffic jam
We're stuck in a traffic jam

This is unbearable
When will it end?
We may not be moving
But we're going round the bend

Traffic jam
Traffic jam
We're STILL STUCK in a TRAFFIC JAM!

Bernard Young

Everything but the Kitchen Sink

Towels, toothbrush, toothpaste tubes, toilet tissue,
    tanning cream,
Talcum powder, toiletries, tie dye tee-shirts,
    magazines,
Shampoo, shaver, shaving foam, shower gel and
    scented soap,
Sunglasses and surfboards, psychedelic cycling shorts
Deckchairs, dental floss, aqualungs and water wings,
Snorkels, flippers, lilos, rubber dinghies, rubber rings
Ram it in, cram it in, jam it in, slam it in,
Push it in, squash it in, there's more than you think
Pack it up, rack it up, stack it front to back it up
Everything but the kitchen sink.

Buckets, spades, plastic rakes, blankets, windbreaks
Suitcase, holdalls, picnic hampers, footballs,
Cricket balls, bats and wickets, frisbees, kites and
    tennis raquets
Flip-flops, fizzy pop, thermos flask and ice box
Anoraks and pac-a-macs, sunhats and baseball caps
Sportswear, swimwear, evening wear and gymwear
Ram it in, cram it in, jam it in, slam it in,
Push it in, squash it in, there's more than you think
Pack it up, rack it up, stack it front to back it up
Everything but the kitchen sink.

Gameboy, radio, beatbox stereo,
Portable TV, personal CD,
Wet suits, water skis, pots and pans and cutlery
Baby sister's teddy bear, Grandad's favourite armchair,

Camcorder, batteries, camera accessories,
Wellies and umbrellas and the speedboat with
  propellors
Ram it in, cram it in, jam it in, slam it in,
Push it in, squash it in, there's more than you think
Pack it up, rack it up, stack it front to back it up
Everything but the kitchen sink.

Handkerchiefs with knots on
A shirt with polka dots on
Swimming trunks with spots on
A big beachball with blots on
A towel with some yachts on
A Summer guide of "What's On"
To remind us what a lot's on
So ram it in, cram it in, jam it in, slam it in,
Pack it up, rack it up, stack it front to back it up,
Push it in, squash it in, that should be just everything
Nothing we've forgotten, nothing we're without
With everything but the kitchen sink
We've all we need for a nice day out!

Paul Cookson

20
BIRTHDAYS

My Birthday was a Blast

My birthday was a *blast* this year –
we all had so much fun,
that, next year, I've decided
to have *another* one!

Ted Scheu

Walkies

Dog years tick tock tick quicker
than human years, they say,

so please excuse me if I pant
and take my time, today:

it's not my fault. I *ran*
before you walked or learnt to play.

By the time you started school,
I was turning slightly grey.

Blame nature and not me
if I'm past doggy middle-age;

my book's nearing the end,
you're still on the second page.

Let me sniff a little longer,
shuffling through leaves –

Autumn is my favourite time...
Soon Spring's blooms you'll breathe:

think of me, as you walk here, then,
our marvellous memories;

all that fun together, chasing,
running round these trees!

Yes, there's a reason why I'll pant
and take my time, today:

dog years tick tock tick quicker
than human years, they say.

Mike Johnson

It's Someone's Birthday Every Day

It's someone's birthday every day,

    So.
Give someone each day the gift of a smile
To help them step over life's misery's stile.

Give someone each day a listening ear,
Let them talk out their pain and their fear.

Give someone each day a warm kindly word,
Let your own troubles stay secret, unheard.

Give someone each day a piece of your heart
For loving and giving was our Lord's great art.

Give someone each day the gift of your love,
As you would expect it from Him up above.

For your gifts are God's gifts to spread among others
And we are God's people – all sisters and brothers.

Frank Keetley

Birthday Bike

For my birthday gift
I had a brand-new bike
With eighteen gears,
   Alloy wheels,
   Lights!

That night I should have slept
But found myself in Space.
I cycled past Mars
   To the stars,
   It was ace!

I didn't fall (not once)
Just kept on pedalling,
The spokes sparkling silver,
   The dark chain
   Humming.

I reached the Milky Way,
Whizzed up its spangled lanes,
Alone, but so happy!
   Then free-wheeled
   Down again.

Through my open window
I came riding in
Asleep, still in the saddle
   Just as dawn
   Was sliding in!

Ivan Jones

Birthday

I open my eyes
And think what's today?
And then I remember
Today I'm ten!
I wonder what time I was born;
Strange being a year older
Than I was yesterday.
For an hour I feel superior
Happy, excited, strange
Then everybody else comes into my life
And I realise I'm just the same as yesterday.
I wake my sister Sophie up
She has crust around her eyes
And sleeps all crooked
With her bum up in the air.
'It's my birthday!' I shout.
'Brilliant,' she says and dozes off again.
I think I'm special
But no one else seems to be impressed.
I look through the window at the swing,
The climbing frame,
The hazel and the apple trees.
The sun shines on the patio
And on the pond and the huge oak
At the bottom of the garden.
I hear the wheels of the train
From Four Oaks
Making for Birmingham.
Soon in September
I'll be going to King Edward's
Starting a new life.

Gareth Owen

Elroy had a Football Cake

Elroy had a football cake –
It took his mum all afternoon to bake.

And to make it look just right.
Lots of icing – black and white,

It looked dead real – a clever fake
Then dopey Eric thought he'd take

A swing at it, give it a kick...
It was a really stupid trick.

His foot stuck in the cream – real thick –
Cream and toes? Made me feel sick.

Eric shouted '*Goal*!' but Elroy cried.
His cake was wrecked with Eric's foot inside.

It was a shame – that cake so good and sweet
Should be stuffed full of Eric's cheesy feet.

Jan Dean

Countdown

Five months
Four months
Three months
Two months
One more month to wait,
I'm counting down from being seven
And up to being eight.

Three weeks
Two weeks
One week
One day
It's here, it's here at last,
My day of days,
My birthday,
And it's whizzing by so fast.

Birthday cards
Birthday presents
Birthday candles
Birthday cake,
Birthday party
Birthday bingeing
Birthday bedtime tummy ache.

And though it's perfect being eight,
A thought has crossed my mind,
In eleven months and thirty days
Exactly, I'll be nine.

Daphne Kitching

Happy Birthday

A ticket for a cancelled match,
A jar of milk and fish oil,
A half-chewed toffee from last year
Neatly wrapped in tin foil.

A year's supply of cabbage soup,
A plate of monkey claws,
A two man tent with Micky Drupp
Who snores and snores and snores

A watch that loses hours
Every single minute,
A jar of wildflower honey
With twenty bees still in it,

A cream that makes your bottom itch,
A wet kiss from our mother:
Just some of the presents
I'd love to give my brother!

David Kitchen

Double Birthday

We had a double birthday party,
A fabulous family do,
Last Saturday when I was seven
And Gran was fifty two.
And they all came:
Mum and Dad, of course,
My brothers Keith and Nev,
My other Gran, two Grandads,
Uncles Alan and Gus and Kev;
Three aunties: Marilyn, Jane and Di
And, would you believe, six cousins.
How many altogether, I wonder...
I know it seemed like dozens.
We ate and drank and sang and laughed
Till everyone's face was red.
It was nearly half past midnight
Before I went to bed.

Eric Finney

Winks

I love my old great-grandma
with that twinkle in her eyes.
It's rotten that she's weak
   and awful thin.
Her face is deeply wrinkled now
in places where she smiles,
and silver whiskers
   quiver on her chin.

My old great-gran and I
have many secrets that we share.
We whisper them
   when no-one else is near.
But as Great-Gran is going deaf
I have to get up close,
then *SHOUT* my secret whispers
   in her ear.

And sometimes,
when we're on our own,
she grins with both her teeth,
and gently presses money
   in my hand.
She doesn't speak.
There is no need to tell me it's for sweets.
She simply winks,
   and knows I'll understand.

Tomorrow is her birthday.
She'll be ninety-six, I think.
Her birthday cake is iced
   in pink and white.
She'll get some woolly slippers
and a shawl from Mum and Dad,
and whiskey in her milky drink
   at night.

I've bought her jelly babies
with the pound she gave me last.
She'll suck them,
   watching telly with her drink.
I know she can't eat *all* of them;
I'll have to help her out.
I'll sit beside her, open-mouthed...
   and wink.

                    Barry Buckingham

February the Fifteenth

February the fifteenth
What's remarkable about that?
Another nonedescript winter's day
Bare trees, cold wind, drizzly rain
Clouds of dreary grey

But in our house
February the fifteenth
Is brilliant
Like a blazing sun
Bursting through the rain clouds
Lighting everything up
With happy colours.

My baby brother
Was born today.
From now on
February the fifteenth
Will be Superspecialhooraybabybrother Day

Roger Stevens

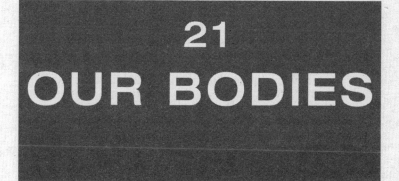

21
OUR BODIES

Bones

Brains
spend a lifetime in
prison, within thick walls
of your *skull*, safe from attack,
unless a bad crack should render
their reasoning dull. To visit, a
vertebrae ladder leads through a cage made
of *ribs* – count as you climb, one pair at a
time. We've all got the same – so no fibs!
Try clashing those *scapula* blades, that keep both
your shoulders in shape. Would these be stronger
if arms were longer and man walked around like
an ape? Don't laugh at your *humerus* bone –
without it, from elbow, below, it's obvious ulna
and radius   would crash with   a shattering
blow, and   wrists   would be
twisted   or   fractured,
or long   *meta-*   *carpals*
could   break.   Test the
index: if   *phalanges* flex,   you may
just escape with an ache. A *pelvis* is really quite
hip, when dancing   away to the beat.
It swivels and   pivots and quivers
and anchors both   legs to your seat
by using a *socket-and-ball* to lock in the head
of the femur. Then there's a need, I'm sure
you're agreed, for *knee caps – patella*
would seem a suitable bone to connect
with leg's *tibia / fibula* pair, one
thick and one thin, then, *ankles* fit in,
meta-   *tarsals*
and   toes
and   that's
where this stands as a *skeleton*
lesson – a framework in which
you might hang organs or
fix, in place, appendix.
Your scaffold – for
body of
MAN.

Gina Douthwaite

Move it!

Tongues wag
Feet hop
Cheeks puff
Jaws drop
Spirits rise
Heads turn
Tears fall
Stomachs churn

Eyes roll
Brows lift
Toes curl
Noses sniff
Fingers itch
Hairs bristle
Lips pout
Teeth whistle

Knees knock
Knuckles rap
Arms flail
Ears flap
Chests wheeze
Muscles peak
Hearts ache
Joints creak

Three cheers!
Better that
Than dead.

Patricia Leighton

Just a Skin Thing

This is the skin
That I've grown up in.
I've filled every part
And look pretty smart.
It starts at my head,
Reaches down to my feet,
It stretches so I can
Sit down on a seat.
It's got a few freckles
That others can see,
And finger print markings
To prove that I'm me.
Skin comes in all sizes
And colours and shades,
And proves, without doubt,
We're all brilliantly made!

Coral Rumble

Hair Growing

Hair grows a centimetre a month
Or a third of a millimetre a day.
That means
That while you've been reading this poem
Your hair
(And mine)
Will have grown
A billimetre,
A trillimetre
A zillimetre
Or a squillimetre!
It depends how fast you read.

Sue Cowling

My Heart has been Broken

My heart has been broken,
My knuckles are rapped,
My head's in a whirl and
My patience has SNAPPED!

My stomach's churned over,
My pride's hit the deck –
No wonder I'm speechless:

My body's a WRECK!

Trevor Harvey

The Man Who Named the Funny Bone

The man who named the funny bone
I, sadly, should explain
had buckets full of gravy where
he should have had a brain.

I know he was a phoney
who loved to be confusing,
'cause I just hit that bone again,
and it was *not* amusing.

Ted Scheu

Nick Toczek

Bodywork

Fibia, tibia, tarsals and rib,
clavical, cranium, spine;
whatever the outside appearance,
all praise to the inner design!

I've a mandible, patella, metatarsal,
I have biceps, I have triceps and a brain;
a pulmonary artery takes blood one way,
then back it comes through pulmonary vein.
There's retina and anvil, epiglottis,
oesophagus and pancreas and tongue;
how could I cope without my parathyroids,
Eustachian tube or diaphragm or lung?

Fibia, tibia, tarsals and rib,
clavical, cranium, spine;
whatever I seem from the outside,
you can't fault the inner design!

Judith Nicholls

Body Language

My legs keep running away
And one hand won't talk to the other
My left foot says she's fallen out
With her outrageous brother

My elbow says it's sick of bending
In the direction of my arm
My shoulder says it's got an itch
And there are no trees in my palm

My stomach says it's angry
And has started sticking out
It says it's sick of being inside
And really wants to be out

My ears have started flapping
They want to be wings
And my hair has gone straight up
Cause it couldn't see anything

My knees are best friends
They have a deep connection
But my feet that keep arguing
Are pointing in different directions

My eyes have argued again
And refuse to work in time
And my bottom says it's sick
Of always being behind!

Lemn Sissay

Cousin Lesley's See-Through Stomach

Cousin Lesley took a pill
That made her go invisible.
Perhaps this would have been all right
If everything was out of sight.

But all around her stomach swam
Half-digested bread and jam
And no matter how she tried
She couldn't hide what was inside.

In the morning we often noted
How the toast and porridge floated,
And how unappetizing in the light
Was the curry from last night.

Some Gruyere had fallen victim
To her strange digestive system,
And there seemed a million ways
To digest old mayonnaise.

We were often fascinated
By the stuff left undigested,
A mish-mash of peas and jelly
Drifted round our cousin's belly.

Certain bits of Cornish pastie
Looked repugnant and quite nasty,
While the strawberries from last year
Were without the cream, I fear.

And at dinner, oh dear me!
What a disgusting sight to see
Chewed-up fish and cold brown tea
Where Cousin Lesley's tum should be.

Brian Patten

22
SPORTS

Ten One-line Poems about Sport

Golf
That white moon in the blue sky, orbiting.

Cricket
Long late-afternoon shadows as the bowler runs.

Basketball
The clock runs down slower than the players.

Swimming
Moment of stillness before the start: water-mirror.

Snooker
The giant's necklace broke and the beads fell on to the grass.

Football
This net's for catching slippery goldfish!

Marathon
Last metre: the best and the worst.

Rugby
Flying Easter egg under the H.

High Jump
The air holds me like a hand, then lets me go.

Cycling
Here come the fastest paper boys and girls in the world!

Ian McMillan

The Power and the Glory

A tribute to the England World-Cup-Winning Rugby Team

The power and the glory
The passion and the pride
Arm in arm and all for one
Standing side by side

We walk the field of battle
We walk with heads held high
History is on our side
Victory is nigh

The brains behind the brawn
The muscle and the might
The iron will to win
The courage in the fight

We vow to thee our country
Believe in what is right
St. George is ours again
Proud of the red and white

And now they must believe us
And now we're here to stay
The legend of our dreams
That none can take away

And now they must believe us
Our banner is unfurled
Against the odds victorious
Champions of the world

Paul Cookson

Bowler's Talk to Himself Walking Back to his Run-up

What? What shall I send him?
Send him your corker of a yorker.
But – he's such a swift pouncer.

What? What shall I send him?
Bowler – bowl your ball.
But – he's such a stonewall.

What? What shall I send him?
Send him his ticket.
But – how he blocks up his wicket!

What? What shall I send him?
Have him dispatched.
But – my last ball was thrashed.

What? What shall I send him?
Know it he said his last prayer.
But – think of his stored power!

What? What shall I send him?
Send him an out-swinger.
But – he's such a rapid blaster!

What? What shall I send him?
Bowler – bowl your ball.
But – he's hardest, hardest to fall.

What? What shall I send him?
Chuck him your corker of a yorker.
Got him! Told you I'd make him a goner!

James Berry

Boots

It's chilly on the touchline, but
with all my kit on underneath my clothes
I'm not too cold. Besides, I've got a job to do
   I'm third reserve
   I run the line.

I've been the third reserve all season,
every Saturday: I've never missed a match,
at home, away – it's all the same to me
   'Cos I'm the third reserve
   The bloke who runs the line.

That's my reward for turning up
to every practice, every circuit training
everything. No one else does that
   To be the third reserve
   To run the line.

No chance of substitutions. Broken ankles
on the pitch mean someone else's chance
not mine. One down and still two more to go
   When you're the third reserve
   You run the line.

When I was first made Third Reserve
my dad and me went out and
bought new boots. I keep them in the box.
I grease them every week and put them back.
   When you're the third reserve you know the score
   You run the line in worn-out daps.

Mick Gowar

A Daring Young Gymnast

A daring young gymnast called Fritz
did, as his finale, the splits.
It raised quite a laugh
when he split right in half
and was carried away in two bits.

Marian Swinger

Spot-a, Spot-a Sports Day

Chuck-a, chuck-a discus,

put-a, put-a shot,

jet-a, jet-a javelin,

lap-a, lap-a lot.

Pick-a, pick-a partner –

link-a, link-a leg.

Run-a, run-a relay,

splodge-a, splodge-a' egg.

Trick-a, trick-a teacher –

slit-a, slit-a sack.

Puff-a, puff-a parent

round, around the track.

Spot-a, spot-a sports day,

what a lot o' rain!

Not a spot o' sunshine.

Call it off again.

Gina Douthwaite

Pool Song

In case you hadn't noticed
I've been learning how to swim
I'm like a streak of lightening on my back
My arms are perfect windmills
And my feet a foamy blur
It took a while but now I've got the knack.

I've swallowed several gallons
And my eyes are pretty red
But my front crawl's getting better by the hour
I'm blowing spurts of water
Like a small exploding whale
And my kicking engine's running on full power.

I make enormous splashes
When I leap in from the side
(It's better if you do a Tarzan sound)
And I'll tell you something funny
Though the pool seems packed at first
When I leave, there's hardly anyone around.

Petronelle Archer

We've got a Girl in our Team

We've got a girl in our team and it's against the rules.
Girls were made for skipping not booting footballs.
We've got a girl in our team and that's not fair.
She won't want to head the ball and mess up her hair.
We've got a girl in our team and it makes me sick.
I suppose she'll do her makeup before each free kick.
We've got a girl in our team and look what she's done.
Scored in the last minute and our team's won.

John Coldwell

A Footballer's Prayer

Dear God,
Please bless my feet
May they kick the ball
"Real sweet!"
Keep my balance
Keep me on my toes
Help my team mates
Out-fox my foes
May my feet
March to victory
Win the match and the double
And may my feet always
Walk away from trouble

Roger Stevens

Wimbledon Fever

It's the wonderful Wimbledon fortnight
when everyone's glued to TV
and many a brilliant rally
accompanies afternoon tea.

Crowds queue all night for their tickets
or rush for a place on the hill
to admire their favourite champions,
their stamina, power and skill.

We're shown the vital statistics –
the speed of each service, the score,
the percentage of aces, the errors
and who they've defeated before.

Powerful drives from the base line,
volley or smash from the net,
incredible movement and footwork –
no break of service as yet.

We become technical experts
and question the linesman's call
when players and even the umpire
completely lose sight of the ball.

The excitement, ambitions and tensions
increase as the Finals draw near;
then suddenly, madly, it's over
'til Wimbledon fortnight next year.

Anne Allinson

313

23
HOBBIES

A Busy Life

Gymnastics on Monday,
Piano on Tuesday,
Brownies on Wednesday,
Swimming on Thursday,
Dancing on Friday,
Horse riding on Saturday,
Athletics on Sunday –

Where is a day
That's just for *play*?

Anne Logan

We're the Downhill Racers

Pushing pedals, setting paces
Windblown hair and smiling faces
Grinning, winning speeding aces
We're the downhill racers

Great adventures, going places
Rocket ships to lunar bases
Motorcycle cops on chases
We're the downhill racers

Thrills and spills – faster faster!
Gliding wheels sliding past you
Hear the squeals and shouts of laughter
We're the downhill racers

Hi-octane adrenaline pumping
Hammer pounding, heartbeat pumping
Wild excited jumping, bumping
We're the downhill racers

Wheels of fire – we're fanatics
On cloud nine – we're ecstatic
Mad for it – we're cyclopathic
We're the downhill racers

The urge to surge downhill's appealing
Nothing else can beat this feeling
Leading, speeding and freewheeling
We're the downhill
      downhill
         racers!

Paul Cookson

Ballet Dancer

Battements tendus.
Arms following
Legs, please.
Let me see no drooping
Elbows.
Tighten up your floppy knees!

Demi-pliés.
Ankles steady. Long
Necks, keep those
Chins up! Good. Retirés.
Exte-e-e-end your legs
Right to the tips of your toes!

Sue Cowling

I Like Collecting Cars

Cars that are old, cars that are new,
  Cars that come with a racing crew,

Cars that whizz along the ground,
  Cars with wheels that won't go round,

Cars with batteries, cars you push,
  Cars that are slow and cars that rush,

Cars with doors that open wide,
  Cars with tiny dolls inside,

Cars with funny painted faces,
  Cars that are really pencil cases,

But – the very best by far –
  My bed that looks just like a car.

Celia Warren

The Penny Black

This is my best stamp
And it's the most valuable,
Because my Grandad
Gave it to me last summer
On the day before he died.

John Foster

Green Fingers

Some fingers do the walking
Some fingers point the way
Some fingers say come here
And some say go away

Some fingers they get angry
Some fingers they are rude
Some fingers say be quiet
Some fingers just get crude

Fingers, digits, pinkies
You all know what I mean
But tell me, have you ever seen
(And I'm not talking gan-ger-reen)
Fingers that are really green?

Well...I got green green fingers
I got green green fingers
I got green green fingers
I got fingers that are green

I can pot a plant
I can make it grow
I can dig and weed
I can reap and sow

I got green green fingers
I got fingers that are green

I can trim a hedge
I can prune a rose
I can set my veg
In nice neat rows

I got green green fingers
I got fingers that are green

My lawn is green
My house is green
My pol-i-tics
Are turning green

I got green green fingers
I got green green fingers
I got green green fingers
GREEN FINGERS!

Bernard Young

Hobbies

Collecting coins, collecting stamps
Collecting cards and antique lamps,
Making music, writing pomes,
Hoarding hosts of garden gnomes,
Shooting, fishing, fortune-telling,
(Finding fault with a poet's spelling!),
Knotting, knitting, quilting, sewing,
Football, running, racing, rowing,
Playing Scrabble and computer chess,
Hunting for monsters in Loch Ness,
Playing tennis, cricket, hockey,
Climbing mountains cold and rocky,
Skiing, skating, para-gliding,
Running, jumping, bowling, riding,
Watching TV, painting, reading,
Even pedigree Alsatian breeding:

Hobbies, thousands, many kinds,
Feeding bodies, hearts and minds.
I've been such a lazy man.
I'll get more hobbies while I can!

John Kitching

Can I Have a Go, Please?

He plays with model trains, though
he'll say it's me that loves them so.

Soon as he's home at half past seven
he's in my room (his "railway heaven").

Sometimes I get to enjoy a go
before he takes on with, "No, no, no!"

He clicks the signals, mends the rails,
calls it his, "great little tour of Wales".

Studying homework is difficult, too
with him on the floor going, "Choo, choo, choo!"

I tiptoe out, let him rattle on.
Even I think he's mad – and I'm his son.

Philip Burton

Kite Flight

A windy day on Crocker's Hill,
Cloud chases cloud across the sky;
Today my kite should heed my will;
Today's the day for it to fly.

And so it does: it soars up high,
Then briefly dips to rise again,
And I can see its pigtails fly
And feel the tight string's eager strain.

It pulls and jerks as if I held
An eager greyhound on a lead;
A mighty tug and I'm compelled
Almost to see the wild thing freed.

Not quite! I grip with all my might
And think for one mad moment I
Could be dragged upward by my kite
To dangle in astonished sky.

But no, there is a sudden lull;
The wind decides to stand at ease,
And like a swooping hawk or gull
My kite speeds down towards the trees.

Luckily it skims their tops
And arrows back to Crocker's Hill;
It hits the ground, then twitches, flops,
A stranded fish, and then lies still.

Vernon Scannell

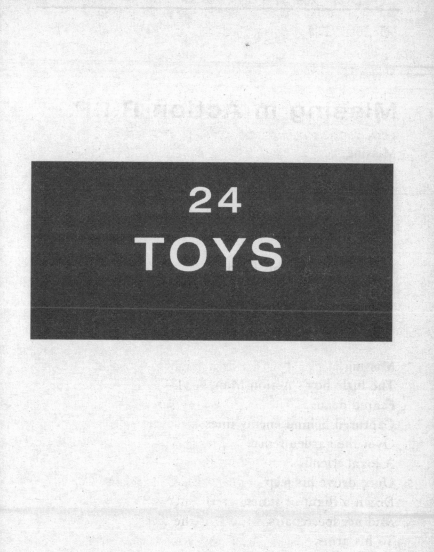

24
TOYS

Missing in Action R.I.P.

Missing.
The little boy's Action Man.
Feared dead.
Last seen on a dust cart,
Heading to the depot.
Brave to the end,
Even after losing his head
In a violent tussle
With next door's Jack Russell.
It's now glued on.

Missing.
The little boy's Action Man.
Feared dead.
Captured behind enemy lines
Over the garden fence.
A loyal friend.
Once drove his jeep
Down a flight of stairs
And needed repairs
To his arms.

Missing.
The little boy's Action Man.
Feared dead.
Leaves behind three changes
Of camouflage,
A battered off-road vehicle
And a space in the toy cupboard
Next to his Barbie doll wife,
(Whose clothes he wore,
Sometimes).

Missing.
The little boy's Action Man.
Feared dead.
Brave to the end.
A loyal friend.
Must never be forgotten,
But already is.

R.I.P.

Ian Corns

Living Doll

My sister was only nine years old
when love first struck her – like a thunderbolt.
Six weeks before Christmas, she fell in love
with a doll.
A special doll that – so the adverts claimed
'...has hair that really grows!'
One flick of the tiny plastic switch, and
'...so easy!'
the neat blonde crop was suddenly
'...a pony-tail!'
another flick, and
'...in an instant: a waist-length mane of golden curls!'

She wrote to Father Christmas:
'Please, oh please! Please! Please!'
She didn't get one, she got
a bike instead, bought weeks before and
hidden in a neighbour's shed.
She sulked all Christmas.

My Mum and Dad were sure –
she'll grow out of it by June, her birthday.
They were wrong.
This wasn't just another craze.
She kept it up, from January to June,
five months of hints and pleading,
then as time grew short
begging letters, finally she left
imploring messages on their Answerphone.
They gave in, bought her one of course.

Her birthday morning –
she tears downstairs
heart pounding in her throat
scattering the pile of parcels
on the breakfast table –
there must be one
is this? She skins it –
Yes! It is!
A scream of delight
and she runs upstairs
into the bathroom and
locks the door.

Silence.
We sit at breakfast
staring at the untouched presents while
up above
the silence grows...
becomes suspicious,
unnatural

then all of a sudden a scream of real pain –
we leap the stairs
three at a time

and there
in the bathroom
tears streaming down her cheeks
my sister stands:
the doll in one hand;
my father's razor in the other.

TOYS

'Grow!' she pleads.
'Please, *please* grow!'

The bald doll grins
its plastic smile, unmoved
while all around my sister's feet

the dreams,
the lovely dreams,
the thick rich golden curls lie
hacked into vulgar,
yellow, nylon
shreds.

Mick Gowar

The Millennium Falcon

Okay
I know
You're right
It doesn't look much
A plastic tube
Metallic paint, some wood, some wire,
But it's the Millennium Falcon
Spaceship for hire

It's been travelling the universe
For five years and a day
And it was built by Grandad
Before he passed away

Okay
I know
You're right
It doesn't look much
Metallic paint, some wire, some wood
But it fought and beat the Empire
For the forces of good

And now, upon my bedroom shelf
It's found its final rest
I know it doesn't look much
But in its day it was the best

Roger Stevens

The Box

There's a box in the cupboard
Under the stairs.
It is filled with old toys.
There are rabbits and bears,
Old puzzles and games,
A broken train,
A doll that my sister
Left out in the rain.
There's a tea-set, a jigsaw,
A few building bricks,
A bit of a bike
That my Dad couldn't fix.
There's a gun bought by Grandad,
And an old cowboy hat.
There's a broken guitar
And the tail of a cat.

The box is crammed full
With old toys, and it seems
It is also crammed full
With old memories and dreams.

John Kitching

A Game of Chance

RattLesnake, Boomslang,
CobrA, Boa, Taipan,
DiamonD Back, Copperhead,
Upside-Down snake playing dead.
SnakEs that crush, snakes that bite,
HungRy snakes with appetites,
AdderS, Pythons, Fer-de-Lance,

Roll the dice and take a chance.

Jane Clarke

The Bike

A month of mithering or so and you were mine.
For me you brought release. I never thought
That dancing wheels and spinning cranks,
As air clung round and pulled me up
Far hills that had only seen before
In hazy distance from our street end, could
Carry me so far from that stone maze
And up on to the moor top. There I looked
Back down at all my Sunday world
Spread out below the hills,
The stubble of chimneys and the mills,
Church steeples, chapel roofs and schools. Then I,
Amongst the heather, was as far
From home as any stranger to the world
And only had to turn my back this once, just
                                                    once
And cross those far crags and those further
lonely hills,
That cloud-capped fell, to be
Perhaps for ever free – until I
Heard the others ring their bells and knew that
                                                    we
Would be late home for church and tea.

Mike Harding

My Old Bear

has been in the wars,
has had the stuffing
knocked out of him
long since,
sit hunched
with shrivelled arms,
droops
limp ears,
glares
a single orange eye
like some tetchy colonel.

Given chance
he could tell
of escapades,
fighting the mumps,
soaking up tears,
getting through exams,
but seems content to rest
on the shelf,
kept in reserve
and not forgotten.

Barrie Wade

Jack-in-the-Box

Jack-in-the-Box is faithful,
Jack-in-the-Box is true,
But Jack-in-the-Box
Is alone in his box
And Jack-in-the-Box wants you.

Jack-in-the-Box is cunning,
Jack-in-the-Box is sly.
Can Jack-in-the-Box
Get out of his box?
Oh Jack-in-the-Box will try.

John Mole

Yo-Yo

Up

And

Down

Up

And

Down

Up

And

Down

You go

**Climb the staircase
Loop-the-loop
Purring as you go.**

Richard Caley

The Hobby Horse

The hobby horse lies forgotten in the attic;
The uncle who made the beautiful hobby horse is
　　far away;
The boy who rode the horse, tugging the reins as the
　　wild mane flowed in the wind, has grown up.
The uncle who carved the noble wooden head is far,
　　far away.
The toy horse lies forsaken in the attic.

But listen!
Can you hear the distant thunder of hooves?

Gerard Benson

My Place

Dinosaur posters, robot clocks,
Plastic toys and seaside rocks,
Cardboard monsters, pencil tins,
A wooden box with treasures in,
Vampire masks, some foreign stamps,
A blue and orange lava lamp,
A pile of comics, paperweights,
A calendar marked with last year's dates,
A spaceship mobile, day-glo stars,
A globe of Earth, a map of Mars,
A noticeboard filled up with scraps,
A chunk of crystal, a bag that laffs,
A thousand books, a watch that's stopped,
A silence where the pennies drop...
This the place where my stories ring,
This is where my future sings.

Stephen Bowkett

Block City

What are you able to build with your blocks?
Castles and palaces, temples and docks.
Rain may keep raining, and others go roam,
But I can be happy and building at home.

Let the sofa be mountains, the carpet be sea,
There I'll establish a city for me:
A kirk and a mill and a palace beside,
And a harbour as well where my vessels may ride.

Great is the palace with pillar and wall,
A sort of a tower on top of it all,
And steps coming down in an orderly way
To where my toy vessels lie safe in the bay.

This one is sailing and that one is moored:
Hark to the song of the sailors on board!
And see on the steps of my palace, the kings
Coming and going with presents and things!

Now that I have done with it, down let it go!
All in a moment the town is laid low.
Block upon block lying scattered and free,
What is there left of my town by the sea?

Yet as I saw it, I see it again,
The kirk and the palace, the ships and the men,
And as long as I live and were'er I may be,
I'll always remember my town by the sea.

Robert Louis Stevenson

25
TRANSPORT
AND TRAVEL

Where Go the Boats?

Dark brown is the river,
    Golden is the sand.
It flows along for ever,
    With trees on either hand.

Green leaves a-floating,
    Castles of the foam,
Boats of mine a-boating –
    Where will all come home?

On goes the river
    And out past the mill,
Away down the valley,
    Away down the hill.

Away down the river,
    A hundred miles or more,
Other little children
    Shall bring my boats ashore.

Robert Louis Stevenson

Shopping Trolley

Scoot down the aisles
in my shopping trolley,
I could go for miles
in my shopping trolley.

Never say excuse me,
never say please,
ram it in the back
of someone's knees.

You really won't
believe your eyes,
my shopping trolley's
been customised.

It's got bull bar,
radio controls,
engine in the back
and it purrs like a Rolls.

It's got a Volvo chassis,
a velvet seat,
and around the store
it can't be beat.

It does somersaults
and big backflips,
roly-polys
and wheely dips.

It does over seventy
miles per hour,
flashing past
in a burst of power.

Scoot down the aisles
in my shopping trolley,
I could go for miles
in my shopping trolley.

Never say excuse me,
never say please,
ram it in the back
of someone's knees.

Brian Moses

Stuck Behind the Man with the Caravan

He's stuck
Stuck behind the man
He's stuck
Stuck behind the man
He's stuck
Stuck behind the man
Stuck behind the man with the caravan
Stuck behind the man with the caravan
That's me   ...*that's him*....

I'm the man with the caravan
          and I'm the man behind
I've got all weekend
          and I haven't got the time

Bank holiday country road
caravan with heavy load
in my mirror I can see
twenty five cars trying to pass me...

I'm two hours late already
I just can't drive this steady
Gotta put my foot down Gotta get past
Gotta get there Gotta get there fast!
Gotta get there Gotta get there fast!

He's stuck...etc.

Is that a gap in front (gasp!)?
Is that a gap in front (gasp!)?
I'm going to the middle
I'm going to the middle
I'm going to the middle little by little

I'm trying to overtake it
I'm trying to overtake it
I'm trying to overtake it
I'm never going to make it...

You're stuck...hard luck!
You're stuck...hard luck!

He's stuck...etc.

A big white "P" in front of me
That's a lay by up ahead
I could make them smile
pull over for a while
but I think I'll
slowly drive five more miles
in style in style instead!

Oh! No! Drat! Blast!
Look at that! He's gone right past!
Goodbye lay by I've gotta drive by
I'm gonna cry if I don't get by
Stuck here til I'm past my sell by
date, I'm late, trying to accelerate
this state is great, this bloke is gonna make me
wait, aggravate, frustrate, agitate, make me hate!

He's stuck...etc

Sooner or later sooner or later
he's got to use his indicator
Left or right I don't care
He could go anywhere
Look there! Look there!

He's turning off just there!
Yippee! I'm free!
Open road in front of me
I'll just get round this bend...
Oh no! Not again!

Tough luck, I'm back
I found a short cut down this track
You're stuck, you're stuck
just like you were before
And I can't stand it any more!

He's stuck
Stuck behind the man
He's stuck
Stuck behind the man
He's stuck
Stuck behind the man
Stuck behind the man with the caravan
Stuck behind the man with the caravan
Stuck behind the man with the
brilliant   *...awful*
wonderful   *...terrible*
leisurely   *...slowcoach*
glorious   *...horrible*
up to date   *...snailpace*
white and shiny   *...driving me bonkers*
Stuck behind the man, stuck behind the man
Stuck behind the man with the caravan
That's me   *...That's him*

Paul Cookson and David Harmer

Epitaph for Elijah

Here lies Elijah
A motor bike rider
He went down a tunnel
Which should have been wider

Trevor Millum

CARtoon

Boot a-bulging, roof rack rocking
Dad is driving, Katy's coughing,
Mum has migraine, Granny's grumpy,
Baby's bawling (Gran's lap's lumpy).
Sarah swears and sicks up sweeties, Dan the dog is wanting wee-wees.
All around are cars and cases, cones, congestion, furious faces
hauling homeward, slowly, slowly, from a fortnight's (hardly holy!)
"BUMPER B O nzer Break-A-Way". We never left the m O torway!

Gina Douthwaite

The Train Journey

The train is running on the

                           track track track

And I'm sitting in the carriage at the

                           back back back

For we're going on a journey that is

                           fast fast fast

The fields and the cows wizz

                           past past past

We're going to the seaside very

                           quick quick quick

And I'm listening to the wheels as they

                           click click click

And we're going over hills to the

                           top top top

But slowly.....

very slowly......

We come to a station and we

                    stop..

                        stop..

                           stop..

Brenda Williams

Travel Sickness

Sick in the taxi
Sick on the train
Sick in the airport
Sick on the plane
Sick on the coach
And sick again.
Sick six times
From here to Spain.

Nick Toczek

M6 Motorbike

Blow through,
drive down,
Birmingham's concrete canyon.

Squeeze the blur
into roadsigns.
Shape the forms
into cars.

Fight through,
drive down,
Birmingham's concrete canyon.

Peer through fog
into distant fog.
Shape the lights
into tower blocks.

Massed blocks are closing in on you!
Cooling towers turn their gaze.
The car behind is hooting,
the lorry in front braking.
Your accelerator hand is cramped,
your brake hand is shaking.

Blown through,
sucked down,
Birmingham's concrete canyon.

Rupert M. Loydell

Bon Voyage:
Driving to Paris

Our
dad
never
got
it
right
before
we
left,
so
we
were
on
the

left,   instead
of
right!

Mike Johnson

Stairway to the Clouds

I took a stairway to the clouds
And a camel to the moon
A trampoline to Timbuktu
And a rocket to my room

A skateboard to the Red Sea
A submarine to Mars
A freight train to Atlantis
I dived up to the stars

Parachuting on the ocean
I rode my bike down deep
I took a racing car to bed
And drove myself to sleep

I caught a bus that flew
To a bridge across the seas
And then in my canoe
I slalomed through the trees

I scootered on thin ice
Space hoppered into space
With ice skates on the running track
I raced the human race

I bounced upon my pogo stick
All round the equator
I scaled the peak of Everest
Thanks to an elevator

I rope swung in the city
Piggy backed through town
Rode horses down the rivers
And ski'd deep underground

I swim across the deserts
And surf on escalators
I rollerskate on glaciers
And leapfrog high skyscrapers

I've travelled many places
In many different styles
Near and far and deep and wide
Millions of miles.

But no matter how I wander
No matter where I roam
Of all these special journeys
The best one is... back home.

Paul Cookson

A Prayer for "Take-off"

Dear God, help the pilot to remember what to do.
Please God, kindly make the engines work OK,
the nose lift
and the runway long enough...
And when you have done all that,
please sweep up the electric storms and turbulence
and sort out the air traffic control people
   (who don't speak our language)
Also please –
in the unlikely event
of
landing in the sea,
please may the little light on my life jacket
shine properly
and can the man from Australia
with Life Guard on his shirt
be in my dinghy?
You will find me, God,
in seat 13A – near the wing.
That's all –
except the landing which I hope you will sort out
satisfactorily.
There was something else.
   Oh yeah –
      thanks!

Peter Dixon

26

COMPUTERS AND ELECTRONICS

Stuck on Level One

Dad's on level six, so is Mum.
Me – I'm stuck, stuck on level one.

Brother's level seven, sister's level three.
Everybody's doing well ... except me.

Stuck on level one is not much fun
I hate going on when I'm stuck on level one.

I never find the clues, I cannot fire the gun,
Always slow, so ... stuck on level one.

I forget which button makes me run
Forever getting lost, stuck on level one.

I can't shoot straight and my power is gone,
I hate being rubbish, stuck on level one.

Dad's on level six, so is my mum
But me, I'm stuck, stuck on level one.

Brother's level seven, sister's level three.
Everybody's doing well ... except me!

Paul Cookson

Satellite

Earth circler
Solar storer
Picture taker
TV maker
Word hacker
War tracker
Sky spy
Rescue eye
Star seeker
Black hole peeker
Fast moving
Slow seeming
Point of light

Satellite

Patricia Leighton

@

I am a sign whose time has come.
Sign of the times, I'm where its @,
a stylish techno-aristocr@.
In all emails, to each dot com,

though no bigger than gn@ or crumb
or b@'s left thumb, the truth is th@
I am a sign whose time has come.
Sign of the times, I'm where it's @.

I am, you see, from this time on,
not just the rhyme in c@, m@, s@ –
it's me you need for on-line ch@.

The web is where I'm coming from.
I am a sign whose time has come.
Sign of the times, I'm where it's @.

David Horner

I Energise Your Radio

I energise your radio
I run your bedside clock
You cannot see me but **beware!**
I might give you a shock.

I help bring light to darkened rooms
I power your TV
I help to run the nation
Can you guess what I might be?

(Answer: Electricity)

Richard Caley

Cleaning Machine

I think I've invented the first ever seen,
All singing, all dancing, cleaning machine.
It goes into corners, where nasty things lurk.
You just press a switch and it gets right to work.

It ferrets out 'undies' worn weeks before.
And folds up your clothes from off of the floor.
It has a wide mouth for sucking up junk
like felt-tip pen tops and garbage and 'gunk'.

One push on the button that's marked
  'SMELLY SOCKS!'
They're sucked into pairs, straight into a box.
A flick of a switch, its making the bed.
Then rolls up your jim-jams and tickles your ted!

The perfect machine for clearing up grot.
And picking up food that's starting to rot.
It has a long handle for reaching the stuff.
Like bits of toe nail and belly button fluff! Yuck!

Two pulls on the lever, and set it to 'ON'
Just leave it ten minutes until it has done.
There's no doubt about it, the best ever seen
All singing all dancing CLEANING MACHINE!

Diane Humphrey

I'm into Techno

machine mad man
finger on the button
never need to lift a hand
I'm gaga for the gizmos,
like to strike the right pose,
fully-automated, computer-calculated,
future-proofed, updated so it shows...

I bake ice-cream in my oven freezer
I blow my nose in a solar sneezer
I've a robot bed to service my head
I pick my spots with a vacuum tweezer
I dry my hair in a microwave sink
I write my letters in electric ink
my video-mirrors as tall as the wall
with a screen as wide as a skating-rink.

If I see a gadget I've got to get it
to pet it or regret it or forget it or set it

I've a greasy micro-chip
stuck to my lower lip
and a twenty megabyte toothpick
I've got an electronic thing
that lets you hear plants sing
green songs in ultra-sonic.

I don't need to think 'cos my bathroom sink
has a brain that knows more than I do,
it can calculate the crumbs
in a dozen current buns
while flushing them down the loo.

I've a burglar alarm with so much charm
that robbers give themselves up
I've a magnetic mouse
that can tidy the house
and a highly intelligent tea cup

I've got machines that dream my dreams
that think my thoughts
that fear my fear
that do my deeds
that scheme my schemes
I've got every machine that there's ever been
and I don't know
why I'm here

Dave Calder

I'm the One Who Rules the School

I don't want to mislead you,
I couldn't tell a lie,
But do you know who rules the school?
My little friend, 'tis I.

Without me you'd all struggle,
Teachers couldn't cope,
Education officers
Would blindly guess and grope.

The secretary would resign,
The Head would go insane,
The caretaker would lose his job –
Coz I'm the modern 'brain'.

I'm the one who says what's what,
I'm the senior tutor,
I'm the one who rules the school –
Coz I'm the school computer...!

Clive Webster

www.ifail@r-i-p.com.uk

I'm not feeling well
I have an infection
I can't seem to download
Or make a connection.

It was an attachment
Which caused me to fail
Now I can't surf the web
Or send an email.

I'm starting to sink
I've no Internet Link
And instead of completing
I just keep deleting.

Don't call me a dimwit
I've had a breakdown
Please, Close and Exit
Please! Shut me down!

I've lost all my functions
So please disconnect
And call the technicians
I'm totally wrecked.

The domain providers
Have threatened to fire-us
For I'm a computer
Who caught a virus!

Brenda Williams

Riddle

I hum in the summer kitchen, a white box of winter. I make ice while the sun shines. My light flicks on and off at your **whim**. In me you hide fruit of summer, safe from the brown menace of heat which thieves its bloom. Water in me is like the water from mountain pools cooled in my frosty embrace. I bring relief from the midday blistering sun when you clink my gift of ice cubes in squash. Cool   chill.

Angela Topping

Hip Hip Microchip

Hip hip microchip
Computer graphics TV blip
Three-D pictures on the screen
All yellow red and blue and green
QWERTY keyboard tap it out
Syntax error makes you shout
Bug debug GOSUB all right
Ignore the bark but watch the byte.

Stephen Bowkett

The Modern Monster

This monster is a high-tech beast
man-made, an import from Japan.
A slim-line foe, no fur or slime.
Its skin, lightweight titanium.
And on it's flip-top swivelling head
an eye to spy on you. It knows
the paths you tread. It can communicate:
transmit, long-distance, video to
monster mates that wait in shops
while scheming silently by text.
Next thing, instead of feeling fear
you've fallen for that charmed ring tone.
And find one sitting in your palm
a dreaded monster mobile phone
demanding to be fed.

Rachel Rooney

Jean

Jean was keen on computer games
but not at hide and seek.
Jean lived in computer heaven
seven days a week.
She stayed in front of the screen until she'd forgotten
how to speak.

John Hegley

27
FEELINGS

AFRAID

It's a Long Way Down

It's a long way
down.
Ooo, it's a long way
down.
As the wind whistles
past me
Weee oooo eeee...
I can see –
it's a long
way
down.

I'm walking the pipe
high over the stream
that bridges the banks
from green to green
the thick black pipe
that runs between
dizzy like being in a horrible dream
and I want to turn back
and I feel the scream
stuck in my throat
like something I've swallowed
and I breathe like a dry fish.

My heart beats hollow.
It's a long way down.
Ooo, it's a long way down.
As the wind whistles past me
Weee oooo eeee...
I can see
it's a long
way
down.

I'm walking the pipe
way up over the brook
I stare straight ahead
I daren't even look
as my feet, as my toes try to grip
through the soles of my shoes,
try to hold to the metal
that's smooth as smooth
I'm out in the middle now
and I can't move...

It's a long way down.
Ooo, it's a long way down.
As the wind whistles past me
Weee oooo eeee...
I can see
it's
a
long
way

down.

Jan Dean

Butterflies

Butterflies, butterflies in your tum,
Feel those butterflies – here they come,
You may be smart, you may be dumb,
But we all get butterflies in our tum.

The President's ready as he can be
To talk to the nation on TV,
But he murmurs, as he removes his gum:
"Got those darn butterflies in my tum!"

Butterflies, butterflies in your tum,
Feel those butterflies – here they come,
It's not just you – go ask your Mum,
We all get butterflies in our tum!

"It's time," the Queen said, "that we went
To open the Houses of Parliament
We only hope we're not struck dumb
By all these butterflies in our tum."

Butterflies, butterflies in your tum,
Feel those butterflies – here they come,
Rich or poor, or without a crumb,
We all get butterflies in our tum.

There may be times you get quite stressed,
But butterflies help you do your best.
School sports, or Wembley Stadium,
You need those butterflies in your tum!

Butterflies, butterflies in your tum,
Feel those butterflies – here they come,
Don't let those butterflies make you glum,
We all get butterflies in our tum!

Paul Bright

Help, Diary!

Tuesday the seventh. Can't let on
I'm scared about that bully, John,
who twists my arm to make me do
whatever he wants me to
and if I don't do what he says
he'll get his older brother, Les,
to beat me up – him and his friends –
one evening after school ends.

I've seen them on my way to school
in the subway looking cool
except when a police car's near
and then they seem to disappear.
They're trouble.
            I can't even sleep.
Don't want to end up in a heap
nor look a wimp in front of Dad
but doing what John wants is bad.

Although I don't know what to do,
it helps a bit to write in you.

Jill Townsend

The One Thing That Scares Me

There's one thing – and only one thing –
That gives me a real scare.
It's not a fearsome crocodile
Or an angry grizzly bear.
It's not a ghost or ghoul
That fills me with fright,
Not skeletons or phantoms
Or any spectral sight.

No!
The one thing that scares me is
Having to tell my teacher
Why I haven't done my homework
That should have been done last night.

Alan Priestley

White Knuckle Ride

Heart thumping,
stomach churning.
Let me off!
Wheels keep turning.

No escape,
want to cry.
At the top now.
Going to die.

Lurch then plummet,
screaming, shrieking,
knuckles white and
bladder leaking.

Spinning, swooping,
sick inside.
Screech to a halt,
terrified.

Stagger off,
stunned and numb.
Let's do it again!
It was fun!

Jane Clarke

Family Split

It's Sunday. Mum and Dad are rowing.
In the lounge there's trouble brewing.
Through the keyhole I am peeping.

"Mum and Dad – what are you doing?"

"Go away. We're only talking.
Have you been hearing
What we're saying?"

Could it be that they're divorcing?
Perhaps with Gran I'll soon be staying.
I'd be chuffed with all her cooking.

"Mummy, Mummy, you've been crying.
And why, Daddy, are you dragging
All those cases on the landing?"

Save my breath. Nobody's listening.

"Mum, I see two taxis stopping.
Can't you tell me what is happening?"

Now by different cars they're leaving.
I'm locked in, afraid and wondering...

Howard Peach

Voices in my Head

I daren't
You can do it.
I can't!
You can do it.
What if...?
You can do it.
Perhaps...
You can do it.
DARE I do it?
You can do it.
Well, MAYBE I should...
You can do it.
I DID IT!
I said you could do it.
I knew I would!

Judith Nicholls

Big Fears

Twenty-five feet above Sian's house
hangs a thick wire cable
that droops and sags between
two electricity pylons.
A notice says it carries 320,000 volts
from one metallic scarecrow to the next,
then on to the next and the next
right across the countryside to the city.
The cable sways above Sian's council house
making her radio crackle and sometimes
making her telly go on the blink.

If it's a very windy night
Sian gets frightened because
she thinks the cable might snap,
fall onto the roof and electrocute
everyone as they sleep.

This is Sian's big fear.

Outside Matthew's bedroom there is
a tall tree – taller than the house.
In summer it is heavy with huge leaves.
In winter it stands lonely as a morning moon.

On a windy night Matthew worries
that the tree might be blown down
and crash through his bedroom window.
It would certainly kill him...and his cat
if it was sleeping under the bed
where it usually goes.

This is Matthew's big fear.

Outside Sam's bedroom window there's nothing
but a pleasant view; meadows, hedges, sheep
and some distant gentle hills.
There's nothing sinister, nothing frightening,
nothing to worry about.

But at night, in the dark, Sam thinks
the darting shapes on the ceiling
are really the shadows
of a ghost's great cold hands and
that the night noises made by the water pipes
are the screeches and groans of attic skeletons.

John Rice

Fear

There are pathways in our bedroom
where secret people tread.
There are footprints in our bedroom
grey as plumber's lead.
There are sniffles in the bedclothes,
there are rustles on the floor,
shadows on the ceiling,
footsteps by the door.
There are noises in the garden,
there is coldness in the air,
secrets in the cupboard,
a stranger in the chair...
      there are whispers
      there are whispers
      there are whispers
       moving near...
and I'm glad I'm with my brother
I'm glad that Roger's here.

Peter Dixon

The Dark

Why are we so afraid of the dark?
It doesn't bite and doesn't bark
Or chase old ladies round the park
Or steal your sweeties for a lark

And though it might not let you see
It lets you have some privacy
And gives you time to go to sleep
Provides a place to hide or weep

It cannot help but be around
When beastly things make beastly sounds
When back doors slam and windows creek
When cats have fights and voices shreek

The dark is cosy, still and calm
And never does you any harm
In the loft, below the sink
It's somewhere nice and quiet to think

Deep in cupboards, pockets too
It's always lurking out of view
Why won't it come out 'til it's night?
Perhaps the dark's afraid of light

James Carter

I Like to Stay Up

I like to stay up
and listen
when big people talking
jumbie stories

I does feel
so tingly and excited
inside me

But when my mother say
'Girl, time for bed'

This is when
I does feel a dread

This is when
I does jump into me bed

This is when
I does cover up
from me feet to me head

Then is when
I does wish I didn't listen
to no stupid jumbie story

This is when
I does wish I did read
me book instead

Grace Nichols

Jumbie – Guyanese word for 'ghost'

SAD

Sonnet

Remember me when I am gone away,
    Gone far away into the silent land;
    When you can no more hold me by the hand,
Nor I half turn to go yet turning stay.
Remember me when no more day by day
    You tell me of our future that you planned;
    Only remember me; you understand
It will be late to counsel then or pray.
Yet if you should forget me for a while
    And afterwards remember, do not grieve:
    For if the darkness and corruption leave
    A vestige of the thoughts that once I had,
Better by far that you should forget and smile
  Than you should remember and be sad.

Christina Rossetti

Solitude

Laugh, and the world laughs with you,
Weep, and you weep alone;
For the sad old earth must borrow its mirth,
But has trouble enough of its own.
Sing, and the hills will answer,
Sigh, it is lost on the air;
The echoes bound to a joyful sound,
But shrink from voicing care.

Rejoice, and men will seek you,
Grieve, and they turn and go;
They want full measure of all your pleasure,
But they do not need your woe.
Be glad, and your friends are many,
Be sad, and you lose them all;
There are none to decline you nectared wine,
But alone you must drink life's gall.

Feast, and your halls are crowded,
Fast, and the world goes by.
Succeed and give, and it helps you live,
But no man can help you die;
For there is room in the halls of pleasure
For a long and lordly train,
But one by one we must all file on
Through the narrow aisles of pain.

Ella Wheeler Wilcox

Feeling Sad

I feel out of sorts
Mopey
Listless
Dopey
Can't be bothered.
I'm a down in the dumps
Droopy draws.
Doleful
Soulful.
A lacklustre
Melancholic
Who does lack
A daisical.
Like a wet blanket
With a black cloud hanging over me,
I've got the blues.
Would I feel better if
I had the greens?
My heart is broken
Dissed
And sick.
Weighed down
Cut up
Woebegone
Sluggish
And I don't like slugs.

Smile, it may never happen?
But it already has.

sigh

Katharine Crossley

Me and You

Tell me why you're crying,
Tell me why you're sad,
Tell me why you're silent,
Tell me what's so bad.

I've got no-one to talk to,
I'm always on my own,
I've got no-one to call a friend,
I'm scared and all alone.

Talk to me, I'll listen,
I'm sometimes lonely too,
Together we can beat it,
Together – me and you.

                              Clive Webster

While I'm Asking

As you know Dear God
I've not been very happy
These past few days.

All it would take
Dear God to cheer me up
Would be for the rain to stop pouring
And the sun to shine
So that I could take
My usual walk in the park.

And while I'm asking
Dear God there's one other thing –
Would you please
Persuade Mum and Dad
To get me another dog?

Amen.

Philip Waddell

The Trouble is...

Like jigsaw pieces from a different box
Like faulty plugs that have a broken pin
Like some odd key that won't undo the locks.
The trouble is... I don't fit in.

Like heavy black bin-bags to empty or
Like muddy balls and boots when adults shout
Like rinsed milk bottles lined up at the door
The trouble is... I am left out.

But unlike jigsaw pieces, plugs or key
And all those other things I mentioned there
I'm not an object. I can think and see.
The trouble is... I just don't care.

Rachel Rooney

Epitaph to a Special Aunty

Your cards through the door have gone.
Your voice on the phone has gone.
Your train at the station has gone.
Your place at the table has gone.
Your turn at *Scrabble* has gone.
Your thrill at my tricks has gone.
Your joy at my jokes has gone.
Your tears at my tunes have gone.
Your share in my secrets has gone.
Your hand on my cheek at bedtime has gone.
Your magic has gone.

All the gaps are filled with sadness...
and with happy memories.

Kate Williams

Remind Me to Smile

I'm sad.
Remind me of
lilac and butterflies;
songs of robins and blackbirds, and
to smile.

I'm sad.
Remind me of
bright rainbows in wet skies;
dry boots splashing in puddles, and
to smile.

I'm sad.
Remind me of
ice-cream on a hot day;
dragonflies and bumble-bees, and
to smile.

I'm sad.
Remind me that
tomorrow will be a new day,
full of possibilities, and
laughter.

Celia Warren

No Ordinary Day

It was the saddest day
we had ever known.
No pushing or shoving,
everyone unusually
      well-behaved.

Assembly, no teachers,
just us listening, the head
holding back tears, trying
to tell us how she felt about
      the accident.

Playtime, but nobody
played. We whispered,
watching the empty road,
where no-one walked this
      summer morning.

The village held its breath.
We stood by the gate, cooks,
cleaners, caretaker, teachers,
children. We waited together
      in silence.

Then, 'He's coming! Adrian's
coming!' one of the little ones
called. Glittering like glass,
a long black car, inched
      round the corner.

In the back, a small coffin,
buried under a mound of
flowers. Then came the cars
full of familiar people in
      unfamiliar black.

They slid past the school.
'A five-minute run-around,
then inside!' the duty teacher
said. Released, we tumbled on
      to the grass.

The day struggled back to
nearly-normal. At home-time,
parents grabbed our hands
and the ice-cream van had
      few customers.

Moira Andrew

The World is Dark when all My Friends Grow Cold

The world is dark when all my friends grow cold,
And icy stares show no sign of a thaw,
And even Ben believes the lies he's told.

The gossip is protected like it's gold
And each will add to it a little more;
The world is dark when all my friends grow cold.

The hurtful lies soon grow a hundred-fold.
I hear my name when passing by each door,
And even Ben believes the lies he's told.

Now all the fragile memories I hold
Of loyal friends are broken on the floor;
The world is dark when all my friends grow cold.

I realise my secrets have been sold,
My heart is rubbed with sadness 'til it's raw.
And even Ben believes the lies he's told.

Mum says that I must learn to be more bold,
Dad says life's tough, I have to know the score;
But the world is dark when all my friends grow cold,
And even Ben believes the lies he's told.

Coral Rumble

Marmalade

He's buried in the bushes,
with dockleaves round his grave,
A crimecat desperado
and his name was Marmalade.
He's the cat that caught the pigeon,
that stole the neighbour's meat...,
and tore the velvet curtains
and stained the satin seat.
He's the cat that spoilt the laundry,
he's the cat that spilt the stew,
and chased the lady's poodle
and scratched her daughter too.

But –
No more we'll hear his cat-flap,
or scratches at the door,
or see him at the window,
or hear his catnap snore.
So –
Ring his grave with pebbles,
erect a noble sign –
For here lies Mr Marmalade
and Marmalade was MINE.

Peter Dixon

HAPPY

The Best!

It's better than chips,
better than chicken soup on winter nights,
staying up late, getting up late.

It's better than diving into the pool,
watching telly in wet playtimes,
frightening my sister with a spider.

It's better than Inset days,
birthday, holidays
and deep-fried battered Mars bars.

It's better than racing the dog,
better than the *Beano*, sleeping at Gran's,
every Christmas present I've ever had.

I'M IN THE SCHOOL TEAM!!!

Alison Chisholm

A Happy Kenning

It's a...
Face-Quaker,
Head-Shaker,
Chin-Jiggler
Body-Wriggler,
Knee-Slapper,
Hand-Flapper,
Eye-Mopper,
Tantrum-Stopper,
Frown-Cheater,
Gloom-Beater,
Ice-Breaker,
Friend-Maker,
Mood-Shifter,
Spirit-Lifter,
Joy-Bringer,
Heart-Singer,
LAUGH!

Clare Bevan

What's my Name?

I'm the sun that lights the playground before the
   day begins
I'm the smiles when teacher cracks a joke. I'm the
   giggles and the grins.
In assembly I'm the trophy that the winning
   team collects
In you maths book I'm the page of sums where every
   one's correct
I'm the pure blue sky and leafy green that wins the
   prize in art
I'm steamy, creamy custard dribbling down cook's
   jam tart
I'm the noise of playtime rising through the
   stratosphere
I'm the act of kindness when you lent your kit to Mia
I'm the star you were awarded for your startling
   poetry
I'm the school gates swinging open on the stroke of
   half-past three
If you look for me, you'll find me. What's my name?
   Can you guess?
I live just round the corner and my name is
   Happiness.

Roger Stevens

A Pat on the Back

I never thought I'd do it
but now I am delighted.
When I was first invited
to go for it I knew it
would be hard to get through it
but Mum was so excited.
I never thought I'd do it;
but now I am delighted.
I got in such a stew it
went wrong first, then it righted;
but I stood and recited
my piece when it came to it.
I never thought I'd do it
but now I am delighted.

Jill Townsend

Helter-Skelter

```
    w H
       e e
    e  L
       T  e
             e
       e e e
      e R
           -
   e      
        e  S
    e      
        e  K
           e e e
       e e e
          L e
             e
        T
         e e e
       e R
         e e e e e e e e e e !
```

Mike Johnson

On a Swing

Higher than houses,
higher than trees,
as light as a feather
that floats on the breeze,
swooping and soaring,
I'm swinging so high
that my head's in the clouds
and my toes touch the sky.

I throw back my head
And the world starts to whirl,
Around me the universe
Billows and swirls.
The earth ebbs and flows,
All creation is spun,
And, spinning through space,
I orbit the sun.

I follow bright comets
Flitting through time,
Past, present and future
All inter-twine.
It's hard to re-enter,
To let go, and jump,
And fly through the air
Back to Earth, with a thump.

Jane Clarke

Caribbean Carnival Cavalcade

Face-painted folk start the celebrations
  carnival is here so congratulations.
Festive fun and jubilations
  so skip along friend, get in circulation!
  Watch out for *balloons and booms*
     whooshes and zooms
     steel pan play
     on a sundance day
     balls and hoops
     clowns fall, whoops!
     red-nosed faces
     playing catch and chases.

Teddy bear girls and puppet show boys,
  A day of laughter, cheers and noise.
Yo-yoing dads are playing with toys,
  dancing mums in clown convoys!
  Here come the poppers and streamers
     pop song screamers
     comics and cakes
     slimy trick snakes
     limbo dancers
     rocking horse prancers
     banjos and bingo
     badges by jingo!

Lipsticked lips, a painted face,
  coconut shies and a skipping race.
Dress up as a nurse or a monster from space,
  joy and fun are commonplace!
  Let's see some skylark pranks
        robot clanks
        leapfrog razzles
        sunshine dazzles
        circus mime
        busker time
        slapstick fun
        mara-fun run
        people at play
        on
            Caribbean
                Carnival
                    Cavalcade day!!!

John Rice

Hospice

Nice word, 'Hospice'.
Sort of tickle-the-lip
make-you-smile
kind of word.

Auntie Win is in a hospice
sleepy head
cosy bed
friends and flowers
comfy hours.

She says it is a happy place.
'Hospice',
sort of tickles the lip.
I expect that's why she smiles a lot.

Peter Dixon

The Magic of the Mind

I've read in books of magic lands
So very far away,
Where genies pop up out of lamps
And magic creatures play.
Where wizards weave their magic spells
And dragons breathe out fire,
Where just one wish gives young and old
Their every heart's desire.

Those lands, of course, are just in books,
But if you try real hard,
Those magic places come to life
Right in your own back yard.
For sitting quietly in the sun
On a lazy Summer's day
You can sit and smile and dream you're there
In those lands so far away.

And as the sunshine warms your mind
You're in those golden lands,
With wizards, genies, dragons, spells,
And cut-throat pirate bands.
You're saving damsels in distress,
You're fighting deadly duels,
You're banqueting in marbled halls,
You're decked in priceless jewels.

You're there, you're there, no need for books,
So real and oh so clear,
So marvellous and so magical,
To touch and smell and hear.
Just sitting there in golden sun
You leave your cares behind,
And go to magic places
In the Magic of the Mind.

Clive Webster

Special is Special

A special time can happen
so sudden
like unexpected win
of the hardest race.

A special time can bring
great friendships
carrying a trophy
and a chocolate cake for you.

A special time comes
and makes your stomach chuckle
with every good time
shining there on your face.

James Berry

407

Joy at the Sound

Joy at the silver birch in the morning sunshine
Joy at the spring-green of its fingertips

Joy at the swirl of cold milk in the blue bowl
Joy at the blink of its bubbles

Joy at the cat revving up on the lawn
Joy at the frogs that leapfrog to freedom

Joy at the screen as it fizzes to life
Joy at The Simpsons, Lisa and Bart

Joy at the dentist: 'Fine, see you next year'
Joy at the school gates: 'Closed'

Joy at the silver withholding the chocolate
Joy at the poem, two verses to go

Joy at the zing of the strings of the racquet
Joy at the bounce of the bright yellow ball

Joy at the key unlocking the door
Joy at the sound of her voice in the hall.

Roger McGough

Joy

He who binds to himself a joy
Does the wingéd life destroy;
But he who kisses the joy as it flies
Lives in eternity's sun rise.

William Blake

ANGRY

The Shouting Side

There's a war being waged
in our family,
Mum versus Dad,
in the middle there's me
and it's hard to decide
whose side I'm on
when they're both
on the shouting side.

Dad shouts at mum,
mum screams at dad,
then they start on me
and it makes me mad,
I don't want to decide
whose side I'm on
when they're both
on the shouting side.

Can't they see,
can't they be quiet?
Why do they yell
like they're starting a riot.
They're acting this out
on a tiny stage,
there's no need to shout
or fly into a rage.

There's no need to take out
their feelings on me,
I'm trying to listen,
can't they see.
I'm standing here
with my ears wide open,
somebody please
be quietly spoken.

There's a war being waged
in our family,
Mum versus Dad,
in the middle there's me
and it's hard to decide
whose side I'm on
when they're both
on the shouting side.

Brian Moses

Huff

I am in a tremendous huff –
Really, really bad.
It isn't any ordinary huff –
It's one of the best I've had.

I plan to keep it up for a month
Or maybe for a year
And you needn't think you can make me smile
Or talk to you. No fear.

I can do without you and her and them –
Too late to make amends.
I'll think deep thoughts on my own for a while,
Then find some better friends.

And they'll be wise and kind and good
And bright enough to see
That they should behave with proper respect
Towards somebody like me.

I do like being in a huff –
cold fury is so heady.
I've been like this for half an hour
And it's cheered me up already.

Perhaps I'll give them another chance,
Now I'm feeling stronger
But they'd better watch out – my next big huff
Could last, much, much, much longer.

Wendy Cope

Just Do

fall out of bed   swear
rip of pyjamas   swear
throw on clothes   swear
stomp into kitchen   swear
eat meat pie   swear
stomp outside   swear
slam door   swear
stomp to school   swear
push kids   swear
stomp into classroom   swear
throw bag on floor   swear
give kids hidings   swear
fight teachers   swear
storm out of school   swear
stomp through streets

no reason
just do

Nicholas Oram

Cross Words

```
        t
  t    wham
  rip   r    d
  i    a  twist    s s  scrap
  poke  s  h gu    slang h
    i  shout  grip    a a  u
  b claw  m c  u    spit  c
wreck  e  pull   n  n choke
h a  shake   o  s c  a h
a t   n r   hurl hurt
c  s e  stab t i    l
k  wrench  i   n j
   a  r o  f s  grab
   t  rave flog  bang
 b    a  e  c     t
 a    n  knock   hit
 scratch   u    let's
 h        f     be
          f     e
                s
              mates
```

Gina Douthwaite

GRRRR!

If you try to calm me down,
I will roll round on the ground.
If you try to make me stop,
I will scream until I pop,
If you shh! me, I will shout,
Till it makes my eyes pop out.

Refrain:
I don't want to! I don't like you!
If you touch me, I will bite you!

If you smile then I will glare,
If you're sad then I don't care.
If you tidy up my desk,
I'll come back and make a mess.
If you tell me I've been bad,
I will say, 'Oh good, I'm glad!'

Refrain:
I don't want to! I don't like you!
If you touch me, I will bite you!

If you bake a chocolate cake,
I'll put in some fishing bait.
If you make some lemonade,
I'll stir some mud in with a spade.
If you sing a lullaby,
I'll join in – the key of Y!

Refrain:
I don't want to! I don't like you!
If you touch me, I will bite you!

I'm the worst you've ever seen,
I'm the worst there's ever been.
I'm a single-handed riot,
Now I'm ready to be quiet.

Francesca Beard

Anger

I'm wanting to punch the world into pieces,
Lie back on the grass and scream.
Wipe the smiles off everyone's faces,
Banish them into a dream.

The red hot feeling inside me is growing,
The hatred I have makes me cry.
I want to kick out, to hurt them real bad,
Calm down, calm down you reply.

My stomach is twisting and turning around,
My face is flushed bright with the strain.
Trying to keep it all locked within,
When I want to lash out with the pain.

The heat is now rising, spitting and crackling,
I'm needing to yell and to shout.
I can't re-find peace until it's all gone,
Oh please let my anger come out.

Marie Thom

416

When I'm Angry

I'm a
Huff taker
Quarrel maker

Face scowler
Voice growler

Help resenter
Friendship denter

Pencil snapper
Finger tapper

Game spoiler
Blood boiler

Foot stamper
Mouth clamper

Cushion whammer
Door slammer

Book thrower
Steam blower

Bed flopper
Tear dropper

Calm taker
Peace maker

Brenda Williams

Anger

Anger
Is a red bull,
Charging through mind's fields,
Inciting actions you may soon
Regret.

John Foster

Seeing Red

And when I get angry,
Nearly every time,
Guess what I see in my head?
Red rockets, trailing fire.
Yes, all I can see is RED!

Mal Lewis Jones

How to Solve the Emily Problem

"I bet Emily wouldn't say that to her parents,"
  said Mum.
"I bet Emily shows some respect."
"I bet Emily tidies her room up," said Mum,
"I bet Emily doesn't sulk for effect."
"I bet Emily does her homework properly,"
  said Mum,
"I bet Emily gets home when she should."
"I bet Emily is kind to her brother," said Mum,
"Because Emily is always so good!"

So I said (well, shouted), "ACTUALLY, EMILY HAS
BEEN GROUNDED FOR THREE MONTHS FOR
BEING RUDE AND DISRESPECTFUL, FOR
WRECKING HER ROOM WHEN SHE WAS IN A
SULK, FOR BEING ON HOMEWORK DETENTION
THREE TIMES IN ONE WEEK, FOR GETTING
HOME LATE ON FRIDAY NIGHT AND FOR
SHAVING OFF HER BROTHER'S HAIR AND
EYEBROWS BEFORE LOCKING HIM IN THE
CUPBOARD UNDER THE SINK!"

(None of it was true, but it made me feel a lot better
  and Mum went really quiet.)

Coral Rumble

Beneath my Bed

I can't go out. My mum just said.
Her eyes are fire. Her face is red.
I have to stay indoors, instead,
Until I've cleaned beneath my bed.

I did the shelves. I've done the floor,
The window-ledge and every drawer.
I scrubbed the crayon off the door.
Could any mother ask for more?

I wonder, has she peeped and seen
A mouldy plate or magazine,
Or pants and socks? There can't have been!
It's beautiful – all fresh, and clean.

There are no bugs, or mugs, or mice.
No toenail bits, or chips, or rice.
It's heaven there. It's neat. It's nice.
Since I was three I've cleaned it twice!

I said, "Oh Mum, come on, play fair;
Don't waste your time – there's nothing there."
She frowned: "explain these books, this bear,
This brush, all clogged with crumbs and hair,
That bread, those boots..."

I didn't dare.

I can't go out. My mum just said.
Her eyes are fire. Her face is red.
I have to stay indoors, instead,
Until I've cleaned beneath my bed.

Darren Stanley

INDEX OF FIRST LINES

INDEX OF FIRST LINES

INDEX OF FIRST LINES

INDEX OF POETS

INDEX OF TYPES OF POEM

EDITOR'S NOTE

It is difficult to try and classify every single poem in this collection but what we have tried to do is give an easy to use, child / teacher – friendly classification as to the type of poem.

Many poems can cover more than one category. In many ways most poems may be considered monologues in that they are written for one voice, they may also be narrative poems with a rhyming structure. Also, most poems (with the exception of shape, acrostic, calligrams and concrete poetry) can be performed out loud and therefore could be said to be performance poems. Poems that don't rhyme could be blank verse, free verse ... and so it goes on.

So, while we don't pretend that every classification is perfect this is a guide to the poems in this collection. We hope it's helpful.

INDEX OF TYPES OF POEM

INDEX OF TYPES OF POEM

Monologue

Narrative

INDEX OF TYPES OF POEM

INDEX OF TYPES OF POEM

INDEX OF TYPES OF POEM

INDEX OF TYPES OF POEM

COPYRIGHT ACKNOWLEDGEMENTS

The compiler and publishers gratefully acknowledge permission to reproduce the following copyright material:

Caroline Sheldon Literary Agency, on behalf of **John Agard** for *A Date With Spring*; **Anne Allinson** for *Miss Prim* and *Wimbledon Fever* from 'On the Lighter Side', edited by Peggy Poole (October 2003); **Moira Andrew** for *Letter to my Best Friend* © Moira Andrew, *My Gran*, first published in 'Unzip Your Lips', by Paul Cookson (Macmillan 1998), *Christmas Wishes*, first published in 'Ideas for Christmas, KS2', by Moira Andrew, (Scholastic 2001), *The Naming Ceremony*, first published in 'Patchwork of Poems' by Moira Andrew, (Folens/Belair, 2000) and *No Ordinary Day*, first published in 'Excuses, Excuses' by John Foster (OUP 1997); **Petronelle Archer** for *Pool Song*; **Leo Aylen** for *The Whether Forecast*; **Ros Barber** for *Yeti*; **Jaspre Bark** for *Parent Problem Solved* and *Touch*; **Susan Bates** for *Chocolate*; **Amanda Baxter** for *12 Months Briefly*; **Les Baynton** for *Sssh!*; **Francesca Beard** for *GRRRR!*; **Catherine Benson**

COPYRIGHT ACKNOWLEDGEMENTS

for *Witch* Villanelle; **Gerard Benson** for *Spring Assembly* and *Moon Music* from 'To Catch an Elephant' by Gerard Benson (Smith-Doorstop 2002) by permission of the author, *The Hobby Horse* from 'The Magnificent Callisto' by Gerard Benson (Blackie/Puffin, 1992/94) by permission of the author, *Look With Your Eyes* by Gerard Benson, by permission of the author; Peters, Fraser and Dunlop on behalf of **James Berry** for *Fireworks, Eyes on the Time, Black Hole, Bowler's Talk to Himself Walking Back to His Run-up* and *Special is Special*, reproduced by permission of PFD (www.pfd.co.uk) on behalf of James Berry; **Clare Bevan** for *He and She, The Seaside Sand* from 'Playing With Words', edited by Brian Moses (Pearson Education Ltd, 2000), *Rainbow Rice* and *A Happy Kenning*; **Matt Black** for *Pizza Pizza*; Eddison Pearson Ltd on behalf of **Valerie Bloom** for *Spring* © Valerie Bloom 2004 reprinted by permission of the author; **Catharine Boddy** for *Chopsticks*; **Stephen Bowkett** *for This is the Weather, My Place* and *Hip Hip Microchip*;; **Paul Bright** for *My Little Sister, Ox and Axolotl* and *Butterflies*; **Barry Buckingham** for *Winks*; **Philip Burton** for *Can I have a go please*; **Dave Calder** *for Just Friends, Information for Travellers* © Dave Calder 2000, from 'Dolphins Leap Lampposts' (Macmillan) and *I'm Into Techno*; **Richard Caley** for *Magical Beast, Yo Yo* and *I Energise Your Radio*; **James Carter** for *Shooting Stars* and *The Dark*, first published in 'Cars Stars and Electric Guitars' (Walker) © James Carter and Walker Books; Macmillan, London, UK for **Charles Causley's** *Family Album* and *Frost Upon the Flower* from 'Collected Poems' (Macmillan); **Alison Chisholm** for *The Best!*; **Jane Clarke** for *Black Hole, A Game of Chance, White Knuckle Ride* and *On a Swing*; **Stephen Clarke** for *Diving Lesson*; **John Coldwell** for *Watching Television, Long Lost Aunties* and *We've Got a Girl in Our Team*; **Paul Cookson** for *The Girl on the News, Stuck on Level One* and *Downhill Racers*, from 'Staying Out Late, Playing Out Late' (Lion 2003), *The Colours in God's Paintbox, Trick or Treat, These are the Hands, Everything but the Kitchen Sink, The Power and the Glory, Stuck Behind the Man with the Caravan* – with David Harmer, from 'Spill The Beans' (Macmillan, 2000), *Stairway To The Clouds,* from 'Very Best Of Paul Cookson' (Macmillan, 2001); **Wendy Cope** for *Summer Haiku* and *Huff*; **Pie Corbett** for *Take Two*; **Ian Corns** for *Missing in Action RIP*; **Karen Costello Mc-Feat** for *A Friend's Prayer* and *Roll Cameras*; **Sue Cowling** for *Marjorie, Hair Growing* and *Ballet Dancer*; **Katherine Crossley** for *Feeling Sad*; **Jennifer Curry** for *Glitter*; **Jan Dean** for *Oh Yuk!, Winter, Easter, Canary, Elroy Had a Football Cake* and *It's a Long Way Down*; **Graham Denton** for *Remember, Remember*; **Peter Dixon** for *Seasons, Muuuuuummmmmm, A Prayer for Take-off, Fear, Marmalade* and *Hospice*; **Gina Douthwaite** for *Hallowe'en Pot, Holiday Rap* and *Spot-A,*

COPYRIGHT ACKNOWLEDGEMENTS

Spot-A, Sports Day, and *Bones, CARtoon* and *Cross Words* from 'Picture a Poem' by Gina Douthwaite, published by Red Fox. Used by permission of The Random House Group Ltd.; Faber and Faber for **Carol Ann Duffy**'s for *Snowballs* and *The Oldest Girl in the World* from 'The Oldest Girl in the World' (Faber and Faber, 2000); **Suzanne Elvidge** for *My Mum;* **Eric Finney** for *Grounded; Seasonal Limerick, Five Haikus for Birds, Ode to Chips, I Can See You Now, Miss You* and *Double Birthday;* **John Foster** for *Chinese New Year Dragon,* © John Foster 1998 from 'Bouncing Ben and Other Rhymes' (OUP), *The Mermaid and the Fisherman* © John Foster 2000 from 'Climb Aboard the Poetry Plane' (OUP), *The Penny Black* © John Foster 2005 *and Anger* © John Foster 2005, all included by permission of the author; **Katherine Gallagher** for *The Smell of Melon;* **Celia Gentles** for *Grandad, Skimpily Red* and *Heaven Scent;* **Chrissie Gittins** for *My Grandma is a Nun;* **Joyce Goldsworth** for *Clouds;* **Mick Gowar** for *Senses, Boots* and *Living Doll;* **Mary Green** for *Percy;* **Mike Harding** for *The Bike;* **David Harmer** for *Playing Tennis with Justin, Living with Cats, Televised Surprise* and *Stuck Behind the Man With the Caravan* (with Paul Cookson); **Bret Harte** for *Coyote;* **Damian Harvey** for *Winter is a...;* **Trevor Harvey** for *My Heart Has Been Broken* © Trevor Harvey, first published in 'Mice on Ice: A World Book Day Poetry Book', (Macmillan 2004), reproduced by permission of the author; **John Hegley** for *Jean,* reproduced by permission of PFD (www.pfd.co.uk) on behalf of John Hegley; **Stewart Henderson** for *Talking to Mrs Thomas, Nothing Crew, Space is Ace* and *Snow;* **James Hogg** for *Boy's Song;* **Angi Holden** *for Festival of Light* and *Alphabet Trip Through Space;* **Tim Hopkins** for *Mr Flack;* **David Horner** *for Kenning for Kevin, The Christmas Rap* and *@;* **Jason Hulme** for *Let's Shake on it;* **Diane Humphrey** for *Chinese Whispers* and *Cleaning Machine;* **Lucinda Jacob** for *Autumn Rondulet;* **Mike Johnson** for *Shrove Tuesday, Widescreen, Beach Umbrella, Walkies, Bon Voyage: Driving to Paris* and *Helter Skelter;* **Ivan Jones** for *Birthday Bike* © Ivan Jones, first published in 'Good Night Sleep Tight – 366 Poems to Bring You the Sweetest of Dreams', by Scholastic Children's Books 200. Reproduced by permission of the author; **Mal Lewis Jones** for *The Maypole* from '366 Poems to Bring You the Sweetest of Dreams' by Scholastic Children's Books 2000, reproduced by permission of the author, and *Seeing Red* © Mal Lewis Jones, by permission of the author; **Frank Keetley** for *It's Someone's Birthday Everyday;* **David Kitchen** for *Happy Birthday;* **Daphne Kitching** for *Prayer, Jack* and *Countdown;* **John Kitching** for *Dear Santa, Trick or Treat, Night Sky, Rainbows, Hobbies* and *The Box;* **Patricia Leighton** for *Raksha Bandan, Old Mother Turtle, Move It* and *Satellite;* **Michael Lockwood** for *Shire Horse;* **Anne Logan** for *A Busy Life;* **Rupert M. Loydell** for *M6 Motorbike;* **Tony Lucas** for *Raspberries;* **Kevin**

McCann for *The Dragon* and *My Mum*; **Roger McGough** for *There's a Plague Around, Autumn Poem, Bees Cannot Fly, Wouldn't it be Funny if You Didn't Have a Nose, The Colour Collector, The Sound Collector* and *Joy at the Sound*; Adrian Mealing on behalf of **Ian McMillan** for *Boxing Day Ghost* and *One-line Poems About Sport*; **Trevor Millum** for *A Friend, The Ballad of Unicorn Isle* and *Epitaph for Elijah*; David Higham Associates on behalf of **Tony Mitton** for *You at Christmas and Voices of Water* in *Pip (Scholastic)*; **John Mole** for *Pet Sounds, Bank Holiday* and *Jack in the Box*; **Brian Moses** for *Cakes in the Staffroom, Bethlehem, Shopping Trolley* and *The Shouting Side*; **Yasamin Motamedi** for *Autumn*; **Judith Nicholls** for *Grudges, Grandpa, Spring Magic, Tuen Ng, Spaceship Earth, Bodywork* and *Voices in my Head*; Curtis Brown Ltd., on behalf of **Grace Nichols** for *I Like to Stay Up*; **Nicholas Oram** for *Just Do*; **Gareth Owen** for *A Boy to his Older Sister, New Boy, Saturday Night at the Bethlehem Arms* and *Birthday*, Copyrigh © Gareth Owen 2000, c/o Rogers, Coleridge & White Ltd., 20 Powis Mews, London W11 1JN; **Marcus Parry** for *Wet Play*; **Trevor Parsons** for *Playtimes* and *Periscope*; Penguin UK for **Brian Patten**'s *Cousin Lesley's See-Through Stomach* from 'Gargling with Jelly' by Brian Patten (Viking, 1985) Copyright © Brian Patten, 1985; **Howard Peach** for *Family Split*; **Andrew Fusek Peters** for *Rap Up My Lunch*, first published in 'Ready, Steady, Rap', OUP, *Fire At Night*, first published in 'The Horrible Headmonster, A World Book Day Poetry Book', Macmillan; **Gervase Phinn** for *Bonfire Night Blues*; **Simon Pitt** for *Hot*; **Tim Pointon** for *Now My Green Days Are All Gone* and *Tornado*; **Alan Priestley** for *The One Thing That Scares Me*; **Janis Priestley** for *The Owl*; **Dave Reeves** for *Distant Relative* and *Achieving Liftoff*; **John Rice** for *You Know My Teacher, First Day of Spring, Merry Christmix, The Food That Gets Stuck in the Plug of the Sink, Seaside Song, Big Fears* and *Caribbean Carnival Cavalcade*; **Rachel Rooney** for *The Modern Monster* and *The Trouble is*; *Chocolate Cake* from 'Quick, let's get out of here' by **Michael Rosen** (Copyright © Michael Rosen 1983), and *The hardest thing to do in the world* from 'You tell me' by Roger McGough & Michael Rosen (Copyright © Michael Rosen 1979), are reproduced by permission of PFD (www.pfd.co.uk) on behalf of Michael Rosen; **Coral Rumble** for *Breaking the Rules, Nativity in 20 Seconds, Life Sentence, Snow Flurry, When My Dad Watches the News, Just a Skin Thing, The World is Dark When All my Friends Have Grown Cold* and *How to Solve the Emily Problem*; **Anita Marie Sackett** for *Sunshine Breakfast*; **Vernon Scannell** for *Jelly Lover* and *Kite Flight*; **Ted Scheu** for *My Pain, I Cannot Fight It, My Birthday Was A Blast* and *The Man Who Named the Funny Bone*; **Fred Sedgwick** for *Mr Khan's Shop*; **Andy Seed** for *The Rev Spooners' Shopping List*; **Andrea Shavick** for *The Teacher , Frosted Flakes* and *Ways to Get*

COPYRIGHT ACKNOWLEDGEMENTS

into the Pool - Instructions for Parents; M.Boyars Ltd, on behalf of **Shel Silverstein** for *Channels*; **Matt Simpson** for *Summer Haiku* and *There was...*; **Lemn Sissay** for *Body Language*; **Darren Stanley** for *Beneath my Bed*; **Roger Stevens** for *Teacher's Playtime, Teacher, Call me Lucky, The Millennium Falcon, Watching TV, Night Sounds, February the Fifteenth, Footballer's Prayer* and *A Pat on the Back*; **Marian Swinger** for *The Sixth Sense* and *A Daring Young Gymnast*; **Steve Tasane** for *Boxed In*; **Lynne Taylor** for *One-to-One*; **Marie Thom** for *Anger*; **Edward Thomas** for *Thaw*; **Nick Toczek** for *Sliding on the Ice, It's Festival Time, Nonsense Poem, Poem to Read While You Wait* and *Travel Sickness*; **Shirley Tomlinson** for *Packing and Unpacking*; **Angela Topping** for *After School* and *Riddle*; **Jill Townsend** for *Spinning, Listen Here* and *Help, Diary!*; **John Turner** for *Senses*; **Steve Turner** for *The Teacher's Gift*; **Philip Waddell** for *A Cracking Day, Together Ness* and *While I am Asking*; **Barrie Wade** for *My Old Bear*; **Dave Ward** for *Kidding Around*; **Celia Warren** for *Fireworks, A Riddle To Pack in Your Suitcase, I Like Collecting Cars* and *Remind me to Smile*; **Clive Webster** for *Long Long Ago, I'm the One Who Rules the School, Me and You* and *The Magic of the Mind*; **John Whitworth** for *The Song of the Wicked Giant*; **Brenda Williams** for *Love Me Mum, Give Thanks, The Train Journey,* www.ifail@r-i-p.com.uk and *When I'm Angry*; **Kate Williams** for *Wrapping Christmas Parcels, Fishes* and *Epitaph to a Special Aunty*; **Anne Wright** for *Winter Days*; **Bernard Young** for *TV Rap, Traffic Jam* and *Green Fingers*; Penguin UK for **Benjamin Zephaniah**'s *I Luv Me Mudder* from 'Wicked World' by Benjamin Zephaniah (Puffin 2000) Text copyright © Benjamin Zephaniah, 2000.

All possible care has been taken to trace the ownership of each poem included in this selection and to obtain copyright permission for its use. If there are any omissions or if any errors have occurred, they will be corrected in subsequent editions, on notification to the Publishers.